ARMOUR
OF THE WEST

**Robin Adshead
Noel Ayliffe-Jones**

LONDON

IAN ALLAN LTD

First published 1978

ISBN 0 7110 0681 4

Published by Ian Allan Ltd, Shepperton, Surrey;
and printed in the United Kingdom by
Hazell Watson & Viney Ltd, Aylesbury, Bucks

Front cover: *Late production Leopard 1.* / Robin Adshead

Back cover: *M551 Sheridan, the tallest reconnaissance
tank in the world.* / Robin Adshead

Title page: *Leopard 1.* / Robin Adshead

This page: *Scimitars of C Squadron, The Life Guards, on
winter warfare exercises camouflaged in white and dark
green.* / MOD

Contents

Introduction

Since the creation of the NATO Alliance much has been said about the importance of the standardisation of equipment in all services, but little has been achieved. Of the three major types of Main Battle Tank (MBT) which equip NATO forces, each reflects the different approach of its designers and the national interests of its builders.

Chieftain and Leopard, the MBTs of Britain and Germany, exemplify the design philosophy of each country, while the American M60 is the logical extension of proven mechanical systems rather than the result of a philosophy of design.

Britain, having suffered in World War II a consistent under-gunning of its tanks and a lack of armour protection in favour of mobility, decided to adopt the well-armed and armoured Capital Tank (to use Field Marshal Montgomery's term) which came into service as the Centurion. Modified and improved over thirty years of service, Centurion is one of the most successful designs ever produced, and it is no surprise that its successor, Chieftain, was designed with the same order of priorities for the three principles – *Firepower, Protection* and *Mobility*.

The Germans realised after WWII that the heavy armour and armament of their wartime tanks had reduced the mobility of their Panzers to the point where they could not react quickly enough to a developing situation. As a result when the Germans were again allowed to build AFVs, they decided to give *Mobility* a higher priority than *Protection*. In this they were influenced by the rapid development of the anti-tank guided weapon (ATGW), and by the results of trials carried out under battle conditions which indicated that infantry ATGW would be able to penetrate the armour of any existing or forseeable MBT. In consequence the Germans decided to give their new tank a better chance of survival by endowing it with mobility and agility at the expense of armour which they now believed would no longer give sufficient immunity.

The British realised that in any future conflict their comparatively small army and its allies would be up against mass attacks by Soviet armour. This, they believed, demanded two prime characteristics of their new MBT. It must be capable of causing heavy attrition of the enemy at ranges beyond their own guns and it had to give the British crews the best possible chance of survival on the battlefield. *Firepower* and *Protection*, therefore, took precedence over *Mobility*. Chieftain's 120mm can kill another tank at 3 000 metres, and its heavy armour certainly gives the best protection possible within the limits of its 52-ton weight. It has often been said that the opportunities for effective fire at 3 000 metres in the European battlefield are so rare that this capability is wasted, but that can only be proved or disproved in battle; meanwhile British tank crews can be confident that, should the necessity arise, they can kill at maximum range, and their morale can only be improved by having good armour around them.

In 1956 France, Germany and Italy set up a committee to agree the operational requirement for a new standard MBT to be built by the industries of all three. The basic parameters were a weight of 30 tons, a power/weight ratio of 30bhp/ton, multi-fuel engine, range of 220 miles, maximum width 10·3ft, maximum height 7·2ft, and ground pressure up to 11·3 psi.

By 1961 the first prototype of one of the two German designs was ready for trials; the second design was later dropped for reasons of economy. Meanwhile the French built their first AMX30 prototype, and comparative trials were held in 1963. Both teams had found it impossible to keep within the design parameters, and national interests soon sent each country on its own path. France produced the AMX30 with their own design of 105mm gun. This fires a spin-stabilised HEAT round, the explosive charge of which is mounted in bearings so that the inertia of the charge prevents it picking up the spin of the casing and so dispersing its penetrative effect.

Chieftain of 1 British Corps in Germany. / Robin Adshead

Among NATO countries only Greece adopted AMX30, mainly for financial reasons.

In contrast, Leopard, with the British-designed 105mm gun firing APDS, HEAT and HESH has been bought by Belgium (334), the Netherlands (468), Norway (78), and Italy (200) on top of the German order for 2 000 units. This makes Leopard the most widely used tank in NATO. Its firepower is the same as Centurion, the previous British MBT; while the maximum range of its gun is less than that of Chieftain, it can produce a 50% greater rate of fire. Certainly Leopard's mobility is better. The Daimler-Benz V10 engine produces 830hp DIN and is more re-liable than the Leyland L60 which just makes its designed output of 750bhp. Weighing 12 tons less than Chieftain, its acceleration and cross-country speed give greater agility. How-ever, its protection is less and claims that even the 30mm Rarden cannon of the Fox armoured car will penetrate its sides have caused the turrets to be redesigned with spaced armour. The next stage of develop-ment is the Leopard 2, a radical redesign, with additional armour, bringing the battle weight up to the 50-ton mark, similar to Chieftain, though the mobility will remain superior and its power/weight ratio will still be some 50% higher than Chieftain. Leopard 2 has the new 120mm smooth-bore gun developed by Rheinmetall, firing fin-stabilised projectiles which give remarkable penetration results but which need further improvement to accuracy.

While both Britain and Germany have worked to a reasoned philosophy of tank de-sign it is difficult to attribute any similar coherency to the Americans. Their current MBT, the M60, is a development of the M48, which is an improvement on the M47, which was an ad hoc arrangement using new com-ponents on the basis of the 1944-designed M26. Certainly they have made a logical progression but it has been based on the ex-tension of an old design by gradual improve-ment of components, and adherence to mechanical reliability, rather than seeking to build a tank that embodies principles of battle-effectiveness established by experience.

There are about 1 000 M60s in Europe, in American and Italian formations; Oto Melara of La Spezia in Italy have built some under licence. M60 mounts the British-designed 105mm gun, so successful in Centurion and the Vickers MBT, Leopard, the Swiss Pz61

and Pz68, and the Japanese STB-1. (It is also mounted in modified M47 and M48 tanks and is one of the few items that became almost standard in NATO). Although M60 has a ballistic computer and an optical rangefinder, only recently have a few tanks been equipped with the Add-on Stabiliser (AOS), which the Americans hailed as a great advance in modernisation despite the fact that Cen-turions have had them since 1945. The M60A2 is armed with the 152mm Shillelagh gun/missile, as was the projected MBT 70, a joint project for a standard NATO MBT by the Germans and Americans. This tank had a three-man crew, housed in an excellently shaped turret. The driver had a complicated set of controls to operate while he rotated with the turret. The hydropneumatic sus-pension could raise and lower the entire hull to achieve optimum fire positions, and the engine produced 1 500bhp to provide ex-cellent mobility.

Rising costs and sophisticated crew train-ing, which would have been difficult to achieve in peace time, let alone with replace-ment crews in time of war, forced the Germans to withdraw. After this MBT 70 was relegated to the status of a study. This has now materialised as the XM-1, prototypes having been offered by General Motors and Chrysler. The general outlines of XM-1 are similar to Chieftain and Leopard 2 and show a radical breakaway from the traditional high-domed US silhouettes. Crew survivability heads the list of operational requirements and additional armour protection brings the weight of the XM-1 up to that of European MBTs. Mobility has been maintained; the GM version is powered by the latest Teledyne Continental variable compression diesel en-gine but after competitive trials the US Army selected the Chrysler version with a Lycoming regenerative turbine engine that uses diesel fuel, making the XM-1 the first MBT to be fully turbine powered.

Early production tanks will have the British type 105mm gun. Recent American developments in ammunition give it a greater hitting power using a fin-stabilised APDS round with slipping driving bands, enabling it to be fired from a rifled bore. The XM-1 turret was designed to allow up-gunning to 120mm, and a competition was held to deter-mine the best armament. Using the 105mm gun as a basis of comparison, Britain and Germany offered their latest 120mm develop-

Chieftain and FV432 APCs on Battle Group training in Canada. / Robin Adshead

ments. The British gun, rifled like its predecessor and firing a range of improved ammunition, gave better results than the German smooth-bore weapon. Charges of partiality and unfairness were made by the Germans who wanted their gun, already designated for Leopard 2, to be chosen as a European contribution to NATO standardisation.

The advantages of long-range accuracy and the ability to fire a wider choice of ammunition should have ensured selection of the British 120mm gun, or retention of the 105mm with improved ammunition, in the XM-1 (by this time officially named the 'General Abrams'). However, political considerations and the promise of German acceptance of the turbine power-pack in exchange were sufficient to cause the Americans to announce, in January 1978, that they would adopt the German 120mm smoothbore weapon. It remains to be seen whether any offset actually takes place; it will not be easy to install the turbine unit in Leopard 2 and there will be strong local opposition if the Bundeswehr also accept the Texas Instruments thermal imager.

The front of both hull and turret of the XM-1 are protected by a special armour of the type developed at the British Military Vehicle Experimental Establishment and known as Chobham Armour. The usual American commander's cupola has been replaced by a low profile hatch with multiple observation devices, but the latest pictures of XM-1 on trials already show gun-mountings, and other items, raising the height. It is said that the commander's machinegun will be replaced by a 40mm grenade launcher; such tertiary armament should really be given to the loader so as not to distract the commander from his primary role.

The XM-1 General Abrams is a tremendous improvement over any previous American tank in survivability and chance of a first round hit, and its mobility and reliability should be better than any other current MBT. It deserves the chance of becoming the standard NATO tank of the 1980s, but this is unlikely on political and financial grounds. It will come into service out of phase with the British requirement to replace their Chieftains in the early eighties and the Germans their Leopards in the nineties. It will, however, increase component inter-changeability in NATO once the German gun and American power unit are mutually exchanged.

It is noticeable that the three major tank-producing countries of the West, the USA, Britain and Germany have come closer than ever before in agreeing a philosophy of design and the order of priorities.

Each MBT has itself been developed into variants for armoured recovery vehicles, bridgelayers, and armoured engineer vehicles. The Germans, for example, realising the necessity for close protection of armour against ground-attack aircraft, have developed Leopard into an extremely effective (and very expensive) AA tank, equipped with twin 35mm Oerlikon cannon and sophisticated search and fire control radar. The Netherlands are adopting the same AA tank, but with their own Hollandse Signaal radar.

Light tanks and reconnaissance vehicles also proliferate. Until Britain's withdrawal from her commitments in the Middle and Far East during the 1960s, her forces had traditionally used wheeled AFVs for reconnaissance. With the shift of emphasis to Europe it was decided to go for tracks for the new family of Combat Vehicles, Reconnaissance (CVR) which were being developed. These vehicles came into service in 1972 as Scorpion and its variants. Belgium entered into a joint production programme for Scorpion and some of its variants with Alvis Ltd, of Coventry. About twenty percent of the components of each vehicle are made in Belgium, and vehicles for Belgian use are assembled there. The British, however, retained a wheeled element for long range reconnaissance in the shape of the Fox CVR (Wheeled). With commitments in Northern Ireland, all available wheeled vehicles of the old Alvis and Daimler types were retained in service, and the Ferret scout car is likely to remain in use as a liaison vehicle with front-line formations for some time to come.

The Americans also produced a new light tank for reconnaissance, but although development of the M551 Sheridan started in 1959, it was not introduced into service until 1968. Even then it was regarded as far from satisfactory. Most of the difficulties with Sheridan were associated with the Shillelagh gun/missile system. The missile itself worked well, but the associated electronics in the turret were at first vulnerable to the severe shock loadings imposed when the conventional round was fired and when the tank bounced across rough ground. The conventional round, which has a combustible cartridge case, left smouldering residues in the chamber, and breech scavenging systems had to be introduced to eliminate the danger of igniting the next round loaded. When used in Vietnam it was found that the recoil system needed modification as the gun did not always return to battery after firing.

The Germans used light tracked vehicles for reconnaissance from the formation of the Bundeswehr but now in contrast to the British and the Belgians, they have returned to the use of large eight-wheeled armoured cars for their new vehicles. Very reminiscent of the SdKfz231 to SdKfz234 (8 rad) armoured cars of WWII, the new Luchs (Lynx) Spähpanzer weighs nearly twenty tons, and stands over 9ft high. Luchs carries a single 20mm cannon, with a 7·62mm machinegun mounted on the turret top for use by the commander — if he cares to remain head and shoulders out of the turret. There is no coaxial machinegun, so all the gunner can use is the 20mm cannon. The figure for the number of rounds carried for this weapon is not yet released, but it can hardly be more than 500 or so, and so would not last long in a combat situation, using automatic fire. The attraction of Luchs is its mobility; it has a 390hp engine giving 20bhp/ton. All wheels steer, permitting a turning radius of 11·5 metres, and it is inherently buoyant and swims at 10kph (6·26mph) driven by twin propellers. However, its size must make it difficult to hide and, since all its transmission, suspension and steering components are outside the armoured hull, it would appear to be vulnerable to mine damage.

Armoured Personnel Carriers (APCs) are another field in which each producing country has designed to its own ideas, giving the non-producers a wide variety from which to choose. Both Britain and the USA built a tracked APC to the same operational requirement, and there is some similarity between the British FV432 and the American M113. The latter, built of an aluminium alloy armour, has proved to be the most widely used AFV of all time. Within NATO only France, Britain and Portugal do not number M113 or one of its many derivatives in their armoury. Oto Melara also build the M113A1, a product improved version, under licence from the Food Machinery Corporation of the USA.

One of the early APCs purchased for the

Bundeswehr was the Schützenpanzer 12-3, designed by Hispano-Suiza as a private venture and built partly by Leyland Motors in Britain and by Henschel in Germany. Although it carried a 20mm cannon, its crew capacity was only six infantrymen, and they could only mount, dismount and fire their weapons over the sides of the hull. However, as with most APCs, the SPZ 12-3 was used for a great variety of duties, including command and fire control, mortar carrying, missile carrying and anti-tank weapons. The lessons learned from use of this and other APCs, including M113, were embodied in the design of the Marder APC, which is one of the best in service. It is also the most costly. The crew can fire their personal weapons through special ports or from hatches in the top of the hull, and can be supported by fire from the 20mm cannon mounted externally above the commander's cupola together with a 7·62mm machinegun. Marder is the standard vehicle of the Panzer Grenadier units of the Bundeswehr, and is used as a carrier for the 120mm mortar and the HOT ATGW. It has also been developed to carry the Roland AA Missile, and the Marder running gear is the basis of the Jagdpanzer Kanone 90mm tank-hunter recently adopted by the Belgian Army.

The tank-hunter is a concept carried forward by the Germans from their successful Panzerjägers of WW2. Based on the hull of SPZ12-3, it is armed with the rather aged 90mm gun first designed for the M26 Pershing in the mid 1940s. The JPZ Kanone has a low silhouette and good mobility. However its gun is mounted in the glacis plate with a limited traverse of 15° each side. A clutch and brake system added to the transmission allows the hull to slew rapidly and accurately to broaden the arc of fire, but the vehicle would perhaps be better described as a Tank Killer than a Tank Hunter. It would take resolute (or desperate) men to venture forth from good covered fire positions to hunt the enemy, an activity for which a 360° traverse turret is virtually essential.

FV433 Abbot is the British 105mm SP, now the standard weapon of all Royal Artillery Field Regiments, except in ACE Mobile Force, where the new 105mm towed Light Gun is taking over from the Italian-designed piece which served for many years. Both the British guns fire ammunition with different characteristics from the other 105s;

they have a longer range and a better terminal effect – but the ammunition cannot be used by the rest of NATO.

In the larger calibres the American-built M107, M109 and M110 have been used by all NATO forces for many years. Since 1970 Britain and Germany have been working on a programme of research and development of a new 155mm howitzer to replace the current guns. This weapon, known as FH70 (Field Howitzer) will be made in both countries and it is hoped that all NATO armies will adopt it in both towed (FH70) and self-propelled (SP70) versions.

Britain is the only NATO country which has so far not thought it necessary to invest in a mobile anti-aircraft gun. As already mentioned, Germany has produced a twin 35mm version of Leopard, the Gepard. America built the M42, a twin 40mm anti-aircraft mounting on the M41 'Walker Bulldog' tank hull, and this has been sold to some NATO forces, including Germany. Now, however, it will be replaced by Gepard in many European armies. The British may, however, change their minds. Falcon, a British private venture by Vickers and British-Marc, with twin 30mm Hispano-Suiza cannon mounted in a turret on a hull derived from the FV432, has been considered by MOD for the mobile AA role.

As it has been equipped and supported by the US since 1952, it is no surprise to find Turkish armour has been, until now, based on the M47 and M48 MBTs, with M41 light tanks, M42 AA tanks, M113 APCs and a variety of American SP guns, from the M44 105mm to the M109 and M110. Following the American embargo on military supplies to Turkey as a result of the Cyprus crisis in 1974, however, Turkey started to look elsewhere for equipment, and their first major move away from American equipment since WW2 may be a purchase of Leopards from Germany.

It is in gun and fire-control systems that the modern NATO tanks have their greatest advantage over their potential enemy. Most NATO tanks will soon be equipped with laser range-finders, able to give ranges accurate to ±10 metres at all distances. This range and other ballistic data is fed into a fire control computer and transmitted to the gun controls automatically, leaving the gunner free to concentrate entirely on keeping the target in the centre of his sight. The precision

M110 eight inch (203mm) SP Howitzer and M548 ammunition supply vehicle. / Robin Adshead

and effectiveness of the system varies only slightly between types, and there is considerable competition to get the various manufacturers' products accepted for service. On the whole electric or electro-hydraulic drives are used for turret traverse and stabilisation, and electronic computers have taken over from the mechanical computers of the 1960s. While Leopard and M60 are fitted with optical rangefinders, the British Chieftain has a ·5in ranging machinegun firing special spotter-tracer ammunition with the same external ballistics as the main armament rounds, but only to about 1 500m range. This is now supplemented by a laser rangefinder.

A prevailing argument over tank design for many years has been whether or not the main armament should be stabilised. Points against stabilisation are expense, complication and space taken up in the turret. It is frequently said that opportunities to fire on the move are very rare, and only battle experience could disprove this point. On the other hand, stabilisation gives the gunner the chance to keep his weapon aimed to within 1–2mils of the target while on the move, thus cutting down the time required to fire an aimed shot immediately his tank halts. This capability contributes to a high hit probability and to survival. And it is survival of sufficient tanks through the first onslaught that is (or should be) the priority for designers, builders, commanders and, above all, crewmen in NATO tank units. They will start, in any future war against the Warsaw Pact, at a numerical disadvantage of three or more to one. It is to be hoped therefore that their quality, in men and machines, will enable them to knock out enough enemy tanks to

make for more equal combat by the time the T62s and T72s get within battle range.

Any new Main Battle Tank of the 1980s must have the ability to kill enemy armour at 3 000 metres, to move fast enough on road and cross-country to meet the threat at the right point, and to protect its own highly trained, and not easily replaceable, crews from direct and indirect fire and the NBC conditions which may well cover the battlefield. In terms of tank-killing the MBT will have the support of a number of ATGW vehicles. These will carry the longer range weapons, able to kill out to 3–4 000 metres; the medium range ATGW will be man-portable and carried by the infantry. Again, each country has produced its own version of ATGW, according to its doctrine and its industrial capability.

The first generation ATGW such as Vigilant, Entac, Cobra and SS-11 all had limited range, slow flight times and required skilled piloting to the target. Since the introduction of these types in the 1950s they have been extensively tested many of them under battle conditions in the Middle East and in the Indo-Pakistan wars. Technological advances have enabled the designers to introduce a second generation which is now in service and within NATO there are three major contenders for sales to the non-producing countries. Britain has developed Swingfire from the earlier Vigilant missile. It has the necessary range of 4 000 metres, and carries a heavy HEAT warhead which gives it a significant overkill on the standard NATO 2·3 metres square target. Swingfire is carried in the Striker missile-carrier of the CVR(T) family and on FV438, based on the standard APC. It is not tube launched, can be fired from behind cover at angles of up to 45° from the line of sight to the target and is automatically gathered onto line of sight. It has a minimum range of only 150 metres. It can be fired and controlled from under the armour of the two types of launcher vehicles or, if tactically desirable, the controller can go as far as 100 metres from the launcher, which can be behind cover. This separation capability gives Swingfire a tactical flexibility which is denied to the tube-launched types. However, Swingfire has the comparatively slow velocity of 185 metres/sec., compared with HOT and TOW, which fly at 260 and 278 m/s respectively. This means that at 4 000 metres range, the controller of Swingfire has to guide his missile for 21 seconds, while the HOT controller can reach the same target in 15 seconds. TOW cannot attain the same range, the original version reaching only 3 000 metres in 10·8 seconds, and the improved version 3 750 metres in 13·5 seconds.

Both HOT and TOW are tube-launched. The Franco-German HOT (an acronym for Haut-subsonique Optiquement Téléguidé) is the main armament of the Jagdpanzer Rakete, taking over from the SS-11 missile in the earlier version of the JPzR M-1966. The missile is fired directly onto the line of sight, like a normal round from a gun, but this means that lateral separation of sight from launcher is not possible. The HOT missiles are raised into the firing position from under armour by an hydraulic automatic reloading system from the magazine, which is intended to carry up to 30 missiles. It, too, has a substantial overkill capability.

The American TOW (Tube-launched, Optically-tracked Wire-guided) missile can be carried on a variety of vehicles, but is also used from a ground tripod mounting. Usually carried on a roof mounting on the M113 APC, it first saw service in Vietnam where it had a good record of kills of tanks, APCs and trucks. TOW, like HOT has a semi-automatic guidance system which means that the operator has only to keep the cross-wires of his sight on the target for the missile to fly down a 'tunnel', with the necessary corrections given to the aerodynamic controls on the missile by the sight/computer. However this means that the launcher and the operator are also in the line of sight from the target, and are therefore more vulnerable to counterfire than the Swingfire operator. On the other hand, Swingfire has to be 'flown' all the way to the target. Both systems have their advantages, and their protagonists.

All ATGW suffer from the same disadvantage in comparison with a high velocity tank gun. Even a very fast missile travels at under 300 metres/sec., while APDS from Leopard, for example, is fired at over 1400 metres/second. This gives the tank gunner the chance to fire up to three rounds while a single ATGW is on its way, and also to 'fire and forget', that is to move as soon as the round is on its way.

These are the major armoured vehicles and weapons which, together with their supporting variants, are the shield of NATO (or the point of the NATO spear if you are looking from East to West). Outnumbered certainly, but not outclassed, they are the anvil on which any attack upon NATO must be smashed. It is essential, therefore, that they are kept up to standard, and improved at every opportunity, if NATO is to continue to deter Soviet aggression.

With the cost of development and production rising rapidly, from £1 000 per ton in 1945 to over £10 000 per ton in 1975, it is very tempting for money-conscious politicians to regard AFVs as luxuries. Too many Siren voices have hailed the ATGW as the end of the tank; many military Cassandras say that if it comes to a shooting war then we shall be 'defeated by telegram' before our expensive hardware can be effective. The Russians think otherwise and have increased the number of tanks in their Armoured Divisions and nearly doubled the number in their Motor Rifle Divisions and the best answer to the tank remains another tank. Certainly it becomes difficult to justify the expenditure of over a million dollars for one tank which may be knocked out by a missile costing a mere ten thousand, but no-one has yet invented a substitute mobile weapon platform with sufficient protection to replace the tank. And if it were invented it would still be called a tank. With sophistication and costs rising, the only way of controlling expenditure is by standardisation among the NATO allies. There are 32 separate armoured vehicles described in this book. Let us hope that any future edition will cover less than half this number.

Leopard
Main Battle Tank

Vehicle: Leopard
Crew: 4
Dimensions:
length 9·54m (gun forward) 6·94m (hull)
width 3·25m (3·40m with skirts)
height 2·64m (top of cupola)
weight 42 400kg (battle weight)
Armament:
main 1 × 105mm L7A3 gun
ammunition 60 rounds
secondary 1 × 7·62mm MG3 coaxial and
1 × 7·62mm MGC on cupola
ammunition 5 500 rounds
Mobility:
speed (ground) 65kph
range 600km
ground pressure ·90kg/cm^2

With the phasing out of service of the M47 and M48 American tanks, Leopard is the most widely used MBT in NATO. Six countries have taken it into service, and nearly 4 000 have been built. Leopard, like all tanks, has undergone considerable modification since its original design, and a large scale retrofit programme for the various modifications now in progress will make it difficult to identify the different models.

In its first production form in 1965, Leopard had the British-designed 105mm gun mounted in a cast turret, unstabilised and with an optical rangefinder. The suspension was open to view. A large basket rack for kit hung round the back of the turret. The exhaust louvres were cast, with vertical bars. A later model, the Leopard A3, has a thermal jacket in light alloy on the gun barrel which protects against distortion by uneven thermal effects. The new turret is larger, and built of welded steel plates giving spaced armour protection. There is no basket on the bustle, and the smoke grenade dischargers have been moved forward on each

side of the turret. Light track aprons are fitted to the sides, with a wavy lower edge, and the new exhaust louvres are fabricated, with only horizontal bars.

Internally many changes have also been made. A weapon stabilisation system has been introduced giving the capability of engaging targets while moving at up to 28kph (dependent on the ground) at ranges up to 1 400 metres with a greatly enhanced hit probability. The early infra-red night driving aids have been replaced with passive image intensification devices for both driver and commander.

The A4 version has a fire control system including a laser rangefinder and a ballistic computer, and a new (and very costly) commander's sight which rotates to give all-round vision, while the commander himself remains stationary. The new transmission is fully automatic. Leopard has increased in weight since the original design which called for a maximum of 30 tons. The early production vehicles weighed 40 tons, and with the recent modifications this has risen to nearly 43 tons. Although this reduces the power/weight ratio, improvements to the gear selection and to the tracks have resulted in almost no degradation in mobility. The Daimler Benz engine produces 840bhp giving a maximum road speed of 40mph (65kph) and the ground pressure is increased by only 0·94kg/cm^2. The new gear selector allows changes to be made from forward to reverse while still rolling, provided the road speed has dropped below 6kph and the engine speed to below 1 400rpm.

To cope with the speed of Leopard cross country, the suspension is by torsion bars to each of the seven road wheels, all of which except numbers four and five on each side are fitted with hydraulic shock absorbers. Tracks are of American double pin pattern and fitted with rubber pads which can be removed for combat conditions.

Leopard ARV
Leopard has been developed into many variants, giving standardisation of spares and training with a widening of operational use. The Bergepanzer (Armoured Recovery Vehicle) has a raised superstructure on which front left of the hull is the commander's cupola mounting a 7·62mm MG3, developed from the famous MG42 of WW2. A second MG3 is carried in a ball mounting at the left of the glacis plate and is fired by the wireless operator.

Production of the Bergepanzer Leopard is at the Atlas-MAK works in Kiel, but since 75% of the components are the same as for the MBT, many other contractors are involved. Main performance data is as for the MBT, but extra large fuel tanks have been installed to give a road range one third greater than that of the MBT.

The purpose of the Bergepanzer is to recover, repair and otherwise assist its fighting tanks, and

A Leopard A2 of the Bundeswehr on exercise near Rheindalen. The exhaust louvres have the vertical bars of the early production batches. / Robin Adshead

the main tools of its trade are the hydraulically-operated crane, the main recovery winch and the dozer blade mounted on the front of the hull. The crane can slew through 270° and has a lifting capacity sufficient to remove a complete turret assembly, or to lift the side or end of an MBT to assist repairs. It can lift an entire engine power pack and carry such a unit on the rear of the hull. Maximum lift according to radius is 20 000kg. The main recovery winch is fitted in the bottom of the hull with maximum line pull of 35 tonnes winding in at a rate of 44 metres per minute. This gives the Bergepanzer the ability to recover the MBT from almost any situation. The hydraulically operated dozer blade on the front of the hull may be used for preparing access points for tanks, digging firing positions and in assisting recovery by removing obstacles. It also acts as a steadying jack when using the crane over the front of the tank. Bergepanzer Leopard is capable of fording to 211cm (6ft 11in) and of submerged depths to 508cm (16ft 6in) and is one of the most versatile ARVs anywhere in the world.

Left: A Belgian Army Leopard A4 firing on the Hohne ranges for the Canada Cup Gunnery trophy, which was won by the Bundeswehr in 1975. / Robin Adshead

Below: The Leopard Pioneerpanzer with hydraulically driven earth auger in position. Two rippers are seen beneath the dozer blade and can be lowered to break up hard surfaces. This is an early model as shown by the early type exhausts. / Bundesministerium der Verteidigung, Bonn

Leopard Engineer Vehicle
Very similar to the Bergepanzer is the Pionier-panzer Leopard, which has the same layout and armament, crane and winch. Intended for heavier duty bulldozing, it is equipped with a larger dozer blade and is capable of shifting 200 cubic metres of spoil per hour. For this heavy work it is fitted with an extra heat exchanger in the hydraulic system. It also carries a heavy duty earth auger for boring foxholes. This is normally stowed on the engine deck, and when in operation is suspended from the crane. It can bore 30 holes per hour, each 190cm (6ft 3in) deep and 70cm (2ft 4in) in diameter. The Pionierpanzer is designed for the Armoured Engineer units of the Bundeswehr, and will probably equip similar units in the other NATO armies which use Leopard.

Leopard Bridgelayer
Two types of Leopard Bridgelayer have been designed, each capable of laying a class 50 bridge, 22 metres in length. Unlike the British armoured vehicle launched bridge of the scissors type, the German concept is for a two-piece bridge with the sections sliding horizontally outwards until they lock together before being laid across the gap. This has the advantage of presenting a smaller target in operation, but is more complicated to design and operate. The version selected for production has an articulated launching arm, smaller than the alternative, and keeping a lower silhouette. The weight of the Bridgelayer is 45 300kg, and it carries a crew of two.

Marder
Armoured Personnel Carrier

Vehicle: Schützenpanzer Neu Marder
Crew: 10
Dimensions:
length 6·79m
width 3·24m
height 2·86m
weight 28 200kg
Armament:
main 1 × 20mm Rh 202 cannon
ammunition 1 250 rounds
secondary 1 × 7·62mm MG3 coaxial and
1 × 7·62mm MG3 at rear
ammunition 5 000 rounds
Mobility:
speed (ground) 75kph
range 520km
ground pressure ·80kg/cm^2

Marder is in most aspects more of a MICV (Mechanised Infantry Combat Vehicle) than an APC. It is the main transport for the Panzer Grenadiers of the Bundeswehr and has been designed to be much more than a 'Battle Taxi', such as the M113 or the British FV432.

The original operational requirements for the Marder were drawn up in 1959 and the new vehicle was to replace the SPZ 12-3 family of APCs which were then the main vehicles of the German infantry. Changes in tactical doctrine in the early 1960s meant that the specification had to be altered, and the more urgent requirement for the ATGW and Panzerjäger Kanone versions absorbed funds so that the development of the APC Marder was retarded.

By 1967, when the Bundeswehr had reached firm conclusions as to the requirement for the new troop-carrying vehicle, the mechanical components had been thoroughly tested in the other versions, including hot and cold weather trials. A

The Marder hull is exceptionally well angled for protection; note the six smoke grenade dischargers. /
Robin Adshead

new series of prototypes was ordered from Rheinstahl AG of Kassel.

Following further trials of the new type, production contracts were allotted to Rheinstahl and MAK of Kiel, for a total of about 2 000 vehicles. In May 1971 the first production Marder was handed over to the Army, and by 1974 the bulk of the production was completed.

Marder can carry 10 men; driver, commander, two gunners and six Panzer Grenadiers. APCs in other armies usually have a crew of two or three, and can carry a section of nine or ten infantry who can dismount to carry out their normal role. However, Marder is equipped with a turret mounting a 20mm cannon and a coaxial machinegun, and has another 7·62mm machinegun in an external, remote control mounting at the rear of the hull. In addition there are two ball mountings in each side of the hull from which the infantry can fire their submachine guns from under armour. This gives Marder a good capability for fighting from the vehicle, compared with FV432 or the M113, though the improved version of the latter can match Marder.

There are four circular hatches in the hull roof from which the infantrymen can fire their assault rifles, though they would have to be exposed to do so. There are no firing ports in the rear hull or in the large hydraulically operated rear door, the rear arc being covered by the externally mounted machinegun.

Local smoke protection is provided by the six smoke grenade dischargers mounted on the turret. Despite the all-up battle weight of 28 tons, Marder's armour provides immunity only against small arms armour-piercing rounds, blast, splinter, etc. It appears, therefore, that it is vulnerable to AP rounds from the 12·7mm machinegun and certainly to 20mm cannon.

Since a MICV is supposed to operate directly with the tanks it is supporting it needs the same mobility, and in this respect Marder is up to requirement. The 600hp (DIN) diesel engine permits a maximum road speed of 47mph, and the transmission has a forward/reverse transfer giving the same ratios and speeds in reverse. The suspension has six road wheels on each side, paired in bogies with torsion bar and coil springs. The double-pin, rubber padded track is supported by three return rollers each side.

Marder was designed to be crewed by short service conscripts, and in the interests of simplicity of operation and training steering is by a wheel similar to that of a truck. Mobility is excellent, and the engine and transmission power pack, situated to the right of the driver at the front of the vehicle, can be removed en bloc for repair in very short time.

The vehicle commander can sit either directly behind the driver, or in the two-man turret, where the 20mm cannon has 360° traverse and elevation from −17½° to +70°, giving a good anti-

aircraft deterrent capability. There are 1 250 rounds carried for the Rheinmetal RH202 cannon, and 5 000 rounds of 7·62mm ammunition would be carried for the two machineguns.

Marder has a good capability for giving fire support to the infantry on the ground and for the whole crew to fight from within the vehicle. Although the Panzer Grenadiers normally use the G3 Assault Rifle outside the vehicle, there is not sufficient space within to enable them to fire these weapons easily from the weapon ports, so the vehicle carries a number of Uzi 9mm submachineguns for use through the ball-mountings. The Panzer Grenadiers also carry grenades, mines,

Left: The Panzer Grenadiers can fire from the top hatches or through the side ball-mountings; the rear mounted machinegun is remotely controlled from under armour. / Bundesministerium der Verteidigung, Bonn

Below: The left hand interior of a Marder showing the ball mountings for Uzi SMGs, multiple vision devices and stowed entrenching tools. Further forward is the radio, then the driver's position. On the right is stowage for G3 assault rifles.

anti-tank rocket projectors and other equipment to enhance their firepower.

With all its firepower and sophisticated equipment, Marder is a very expensive piece of kit, and it is questionable whether the expense is worth while when it is as vulnerable to attack as the cheaper and more conventional APC. Given the ability to fire from under armour will not the infantryman be disinclined to dismount and perform his proper role? And if he remains in his Marder he is presenting a bigger and more vulnerable target to the medium and heavy weapons of the enemy. The prime function of infantry is to fight dismounted, and that of the infantry-carrying armoured vehicle is to take them to action with the greatest speed, comfort and protection that can be afforded.

For all its firepower the MICV cannot approach that of the tank, and it gives away all the protection that a tank gives its crew. It remains to be seen whether the MICV has any real tactical advantage over the cheaper and less sophisticated 'battle taxi' APC, and whether the Marder will prove as effective a weapon system as its designers and users hope.

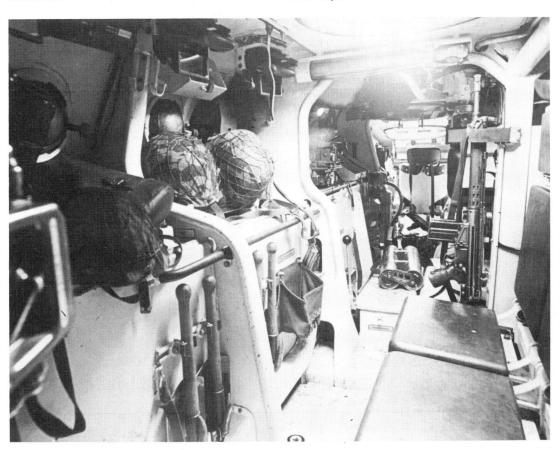

SPZ 12-3
Armoured Personnel Carrier

Vehicle: Schützenpanzer SPZ 12–3
Crew: 8
Dimensions:
length 6·31m (gun forward) 5·56m (hull)
width 2·54m
height 1·85m
weight 14 600kg
Armament:
main 1·×20mm HS820 cannon
ammunition 2 000 rounds
secondary 1 ×7·62mm machinegun
ammunition 1 200 rounds
Mobility:
speed (ground) 58kph
range 270km
ground pressure ·75kg/cm²

The SPZ 12–3 was designed by Hispano-Suiza, originally as an anti-aircraft vehicle. It was built for the Bundeswehr by Leyland Motors of England and by Henschel and Hanomag of Germany, during the period 1958–62.

The rear-mounted Rolls-Royce B81 engine provided a top speed of 58kph (36mph), but its location meant that access for the crew of commander, driver and six infantrymen was over the sides of the hull. The turret carried a 20mm Hispano-Suiza cannon and a machinegun could be mounted on the roof. There were no firing ports and the infantry had to fire their personal weapons from the roof hatches. It was a typical 'battle taxi' of the period.

The SPZ 12–3 was developed into many variants including Jagdpanzer Rakete, carrying the French SS-11 ATGW. Other types were carriers for the 120mm and 81mm mortars, and the TOW wire-guided ATGW. The same hull was also used for Command and Artillery Fire Control vehicles. SPZ 12–3 is used only by the German Army, and is being replaced by the new Marder APC.

Left: *The extra red crosses on this SPZ 12–3 ambulance are exercise markings.* / Robin Adshead

Below: *This view of the SP 12–3 shows some of the interior detail and the large roof hatches. This is one of the vehicles made at Leyland motors.*

JPZ 4-5
Self Propelled Anti-Tank Gun

Vehicle: Jagdpanzer Kanone JPZ 4–5
Crew: 4
Dimensions:
length 8·75m (including gun) 6·24m (hull)
width 2·98m
height 2·08m
weight 5 700kg
Armament:
main 1 ×90mm
ammunition 51 rounds
secondary 1 ×7·62mm coaxial and 1 ×7·62mm
on cupola
ammunition 4 000 rounds
Mobility:
speed (ground) 70kph
range 400km
ground pressure ·75kg/cm^2

The Germans have always believed in the necessity for specialised tank-hunter vehicles, and the JPZ 4–5 is the direct descendant of the Jagdpanzers of WWII.

Since it has the 90mm gun mounted in the hull, the configuration gives low height which makes it easy to conceal and makes for better protection within a given weight. The Rheinmetall 90mm gun is designed to use the same ammunition as the American gun in the M48 tank. The internal ballistics are identical, but the shorter barrel of the Rheinmetall gun (40·4 calibres as against 48) means that effective range is limited to 1 500 metres. It can fire all the natures of 90mm ammunition, HE, HEAT and HVAP, as the tank gun, which is a useful logistic advantage. Fifty-one rounds are carried. A 7·62mm machinegun is mounted coaxially with the main armament. The gun mounting allows a limited traverse of only 15° each side and elevation from −8 to +15°. Traverse outside these limits necessitates move-

ment of the entire vehicle by means of the steering system. The fine lay is by hand, since the limited traverse does not call for power assistance.

The Bundeswehr has 750 of the original type of JPZ 4–5, but the 84 vehicles which have been bought by the Belgian Army to improve their anti-tank capability are of a new variant. This is the JPK 90mm Neu, and the improvements consist mainly of adoption of Marder transmission, running gear and suspension. The new vehicle still has only five road wheels, as opposed to six in Marder. The steering system includes two additional hydraulic steering clutches which are not part of the Marder system. When travelling straight ahead or when making normal turns these clutches are not used, but when sharper turns are needed, for swift alignment of the hull on a new target for quick engagements, the clutches automatically come into operation to speed the turn.

The gun and ammunition system is the same as on the earlier vehicle; the Belgians have large stocks of 90mm ammunition, and plan to manufacture more, so it was economics rather than firepower considerations that influenced the decision. The JPK 90mm Neu also has two additional pieces of equipment that improve the chance of a fast engagement and of a first round hit.

A disadvantage of the turretless configuration is that the driver must be brought into the engagement sequence. If the commander wishes to engage a target outside the 30° traverse of the weapon, it is the driver who is responsible for aligning the hull so that the gunner can pick up and identify the target in his sight. The JPZ-Neu has three interconnected angular deviation indicators, one for the driver, one for the commander and one for the gunner. These have pointers showing the relative positions of the commander's sight, the gunner's sight and the centre line of the vehicle. This gives the driver all the information he needs to ensure that the gun can be pointed sufficiently close to the target for the gunner to make the fine lay and fire.

The other important piece of equipment is the SABCA Fire Control System. Coupled to a laser rangefinder, a trunnion cant sensor and a tachometer which gives the tracking rate of a moving target, the ballistic computer works out all the equations necessary for the type of ammunition being used and sets the elevation and lead angle on the gunner's sight. All the gunner has to do is to keep his sight accurately on the target and to fire at the right moment. Thus the JPZ 90mm Neu as bought by Belgium has the most modern fire control system coupled to a gun from an earlier generation. But the configuration of the vehicle is such that up-gunning with a 105mm weapon, or even with the projected 120mm German smoothbore gun, is quite feasible; in fact it is easier to up-gun a self-propelled piece than a turreted tank, so the basic Jagdpanzer Kanone could be in service and up to date for many years to come.

Jagdpanzer Kanone 90mm anti-tank gun. /
Bundesministerium der Verteidigung, Bonn

RJPZ-2
Anti-Tank Missile Vehicle

Very similar in appearance to the JPZ 4–5, the RJPZ-2 was built by Hanomag and Henschel from 1965–67. A total of 750 units was built. The engine is the Daimler Benz MB-837 eight-cylinder diesel developing 500hp and giving a top speed of 70kph and a road range of 400km.

The Jagdpanzer Rakete is armed with 14 SS-11 ATGW which can be fired from two launcher rails, covering a 180° arc to the front of the vehicle. For local protection there is a 7·62mm bow machine-gun, and a second machinegun can be mounted for anti-aircraft defence.

The slow-flying (150m/sec) SS-11 missile is being replaced by the new Franco-German HOT missile which flies at 260m/sec to a maximum range of 4 000 metres. The launchers for HOT are retracted under armour for re-loading. The missile controller has a single periscope sight.

Vehicle: Jagdpanzer Rakete RJPZ-2
Crew: 4
Dimensions:
length 6·43m
width 2·98m
height 1·98m (to top of hull)
weight 23 000kg
Armament:
main 2 launchers for SS-11 or HOT missiles according to modification
ammunition 14 SS-11 or 30 HOT ATGW
secondary 1 × 7·62mm bow machinegun and 1 × 7·62mm for AA defence
ammuntion 3 200 rounds
Mobility:
speed (ground) 70kph
range 400km
ground pressure ·63kg/cm^2

Left: *JPZ Rakete firing a SS-11 ATGW; newer vehicles are armed with HOT missiles.* / Bundesministerium der Verteidigung, Bonn

Below: *Euromissile HOT anti-tank missile launcher on Jagdpanzer Rakete. The complete missile is packed in the tube clipped to the launcher. The tube is jettisoned after firing. Observation and guidance periscopes are mounted to the left of the launcher as seen. The hull machinegun is not mounted in this picture.* / Bundesministerium der Verteidigung, Bonn

Gepard
Anti-Aircraft Tank

Vehicle: Flakpanzer 1 Gepard
Crew: 3
Dimensions:
length 7·70m (guns forward) 6·94m (hull)
width 3·25m
height 3·00m (radar stowed)
weight 45 100kg
Armament:
main 2 × 35mm Oerlikon cannon
ammunition 700 rounds
Mobility:
speed (ground) 65kph
range 600km
ground pressure ·97kg/cm^2

Since the later years of WWII when Allied fighter-bombers caused havoc among the Panzer Divisions the threat from the air has increased by the extended range and power of the strike aircraft and also by the emergence of the ATGW armed helicopter.

Close anti-aircraft protection of armoured formations in the front line is now an essential, and while the development of the small Surface to Air Missile (SAM) has improved the air defence capability, many countries still feel the need for an anti-aircraft tank. This philosophy has been proved by the experiences of the Israelis in the 1973 October War, when a large number of their aircraft casualties in ground attack were caused by the fire of the Russian built ZSU-23-4 and ZSU-57-2 multiple AA cannon tanks with which the Syrians and Egyptians were equipped.

Both Germany and the Netherlands have decided that their first line defence will be by a gun-armed AA tank, and the result is Gepard. The

Remote controlled test firing of a Flakpanzer Gepard. Production costs have risen to over 7 000 000 Deutschmarks, but the system is so effective that the US Air Force is considering purchasing some. / Bundesministerium der Verteidigung, Bonn

requirement was for a unit with a short reaction time, high kill probability at long combat ranges, all-weather capability and full IFF (Identification Friend or Foe). All these to be contained in a vehicle with mobility compatible with modern MBTs with which it would operate, good protection and simplicity of operation and maintenance.

With so many Leopard MBTs in use throughout NATO the Leopard was the natural basis on which to work. After studies and trials the twin 35mm Oerlikon cannon was adopted, which can fire APHE and HEI ammunition with an effect equivalent to the well-known 40mm L/70 shell. The guns are mounted on trunnions towards the rear of the turret, and on the outside of the main armour. This permits maximum elevation without wasting space under armour for breech movement inside the turret and also prevents powder fumes affecting the crew.

The ammunition is belt-fed from internal magazines which have a capacity of 660 rounds of anti-aircraft rounds plus 40 anti-tank rounds. Either type of round can be selected by remote control from within the turret. The exposed parts of the cannon are armoured, but are of easy access for maintenance. Magazine replenishment is from the outside of the vehicle, and a complete re-load can be made by the crew in about 20 minutes.

The functioning of the unit depends on its search and tracking radar for its effectiveness. The search radar antenna is mounted high on the back of the turret with the visual read-out and the IFF interrogator under the control of the commander in the turret. Once a target is identified as hostile the tracking radar mounted between the gun barrels at the front of the turret takes over. Drives controlled by this radar keep the cannons on target with the necessary range and lead angles fed into the system by the ballistic computer.

The 35mm Oerlikon cannon each have a rate of fire of 550 rounds per minute and a muzzle velocity of 1 175 metres/sec. Both gunner and commander have an optical sight for observation and laying on ground targets.

The continuous use of the radar and the high power requirements of the tracking system mean a very high usage of electrical power. To cope with this a separate diesel engine driving additional generators is housed within the hull.

The German version, Gepard, uses the Siemens Doppler radar and IFF and an Albiswerk tracking radar. The Netherlands vehicles have the same IFF but incorporate the integrated search and tracking radar developed by Hollandse Signaalapparaten. Both types have the same cannon and vehicle systems.

Gepard is the most expensive AFV currently in production in NATO, but it is the only AA tank in use and would prove very effective in protecting armoured formations from attack by ground attack aircraft and by missile armed tank-hunting helicopters.

Luchs
Armoured Car

Vehicle: Spänzer 2 Luchs (Lynx)
Crew: 4
Dimensions:
length 7·34m
width 2·98m
height 2·50m
weight 19 000kg
Armament:
main 1 × 20mm cannon
ammunition not known
secondary 1 × 7·62mm machinegun on cupola
ammunition not known
Mobility:
speed (ground) 100kph
(water) 10kph
range 800km

In a surprising return to the large vehicle concept of the 1940s, the Germans have recently brought into service their new reconnaissance armoured car, the 8-wheeled Lynx. While other members of NATO have reduced the size of recce vehicles to the practical minimum, like the Scorpion, the M114 and the projected American Armoured Reconnaissance Scout Vehicle (ARSV), the Germans have built a 20-ton 8-wheeled armoured car which, at a quick glance, is of the same family as the SdKfz231 and 234 used in WW II.

The main reason for its bulk is to give it sufficient volume to be inherently buoyant, but although its swimming capability and its excellent cross-country performance make Lynx one of the most mobile units in NATO, its armament of one 20mm cannon seems ludicrously impotent for its size.

The multi-fuel engine produces 390hp DIN running on diesel or 360hp DIN on petrol, giving a top speed of 90kph on land and 10kph in the water, when it is driven by two propellors. The gearbox provides four ratios in each direction, and there is a steering position at each end of the hull. When driving backwards the radio operator, at the left hand rear of the hull, and facing rearwards, has full control, and sufficient vision through his periscopes to reach full speed in reverse.

This may be a very necessary attribute, since the size of the vehicle makes it difficult to conceal, and it has little defensive capability. The gunner has control only of the 20mm cannon, and although

the number of rounds carried for this weapon has not been released, it is unlikely that more than 500 can be stowed in the magazines. The commander has a 7·62mm machinegun mounted outside his cupola, but it can be aimed and fired only from the 'head and shoulders out' position. Four smoke grenade dischargers are mounted each side of the turret.

The drive is taken to the wheels from a central transfer box by shafts to the central axles and by a through-drive shaft to the outer axles. The suspension is by vertical coil springs located by radius arms, giving a considerable degree of articulation to the axles, but no transverse independent movement to the wheels. All wheels are steerable, with a complex system of rods permitting the driver to select steering in three modes; for forward travel up to full speed the front two pairs of wheels steer and the rear pair are locked; for reverse travel up to full speed the converse applies – front pair locked and rear pair steer; both these modes give a 19 metre turning radius. However, for tighter turns of 11·5-metre radius all four pairs of wheels can steer, but speed is then limited to 50kph.

The armoured hull of Luchs gives immunity to small arms, splinter and blast, and the sides are further protected by the 'boxes' between wheel stations being filled with a bullet-resistant and buoyant material. But all the driving, steering and suspension components are outside the hull, and are therefore open to damage from fire and mine blast.

Being a reconnaissance vehicle Luchs is equipped with 12 episcopes and both the commander and gunner have periscopic sights linked to the main armament. Traverse and elevation is by an electro-hydraulic mechanism.

Left: Spähpanzer Luchs steers on all wheels for close country manoeuvring. / Bundesministerium der Verteidigung, Bonn

Below: The axles and suspension of Luchs are unprotected. Empty cases from the 20mm cannon ammunition are ejected through the flap in the right hand trunnion. There is no co-axial machinegun, only one MG3 on the commander's cupola. A white light/IR searchlight is mounted on the left of the turret. / Bundesministerium der Verteidigung, Bonn

Chieftain
Main Battle Tank

Vehicle: FV4201 Chieftain Mk 3
Crew: 4
Dimensions:
length 10·79m (gun forward) 7·52m (hull)
width 3·50m (3·66m including searchlight)
height 2·89m (including commander's machine-gun)
weight 54 100kg
Armament:
main 1 × 120mm L11 A2 gun
ammunition 53 rounds
ranging 1 × 12·7mm machinegun (600 rounds carried)
secondary 1 × 7·62mm coaxial machinegun and one 7·62mm machinegun on cupola
ammunition 6 000 rounds
Mobility:
speed (ground) 48kph
range 500km
ground pressure ·843kg/cm^2

Chieftain went into service as the standard main battle tank of the British Army in 1963, after eight years of design and development. Vickers Ltd were given the job of design parents, following the concept work at the Military Vehicles Experimental Establishment at Chobham, Surrey. The first prototype was completed in 1959, and after prolonged acceptance trials, production lines were set up at Vickers Elswick works and the Royal Ordnance Factory at Leeds.

The British philosophy of tank design embodies the three main principles of *Firepower, Protection* and *Mobility* in that order, and Chieftain is the most heavily armed and best protected tank of the current generation. The main armament is the 120mm L11 A2 gun for which 53 rounds of ammunition are stowed. The main natures used are APDS, a high velocity kinetic energy round which is capable of penetrating all known enemy tanks,

Chieftain packs the heaviest punch of all NATO battle tanks.

and HESH, a chemical energy round fired at medium velocity which, instead of penetrating enemy armour, blows a large and lethal scab off the inside of the target. It is also very effective against strong points and soft targets, and has virtually replaced the HE round. A smoke round is also available when required.

The ammunition for the 120mm gun is separated; that is, it is made and loaded in two parts, projectile and propellant charge. If it were fixed ammunition it would be too large and too heavy to be handled easily by the loader in the confines of the turret. The propellant is a bagged charge, to keep the weight down and to eliminate the problem of the disposal of large brass cartridge cases. The charge is initiated by an electrically fired primer cartridge, a small clip of which is fed into the breech, rather like a rifle cartridge. Fitted about one third of the length back from the muzzle of the gun is a fume extractor to prevent the gases of the propellant charge entering the turret. The whole external length of the barrel (except the fume extrator) is covered with a tough thermal jacket designed to prevent the barrel bending under the influence of cold wind or rain on one side.

Above the main gun is a ·5in (12·7mm) ranging machinegun. This fires special spotter-tracer rounds which have the same external ballistic characteristics as the main round, enabling the gunner and commander to range on a target without wasting expensive full bore ammunition or giving away their position by muzzle flash. Normally two or three bursts of three rounds would be fired to establish target range; 600 rounds of spotter-tracer are carried. The secondary armament consists of a coaxially mounted 7·62mm GPMG to the left of the main armament, and a second GPMG can be mounted on the turret roof for the use of the commander: 6 000 rounds of 7·62mm are carried in belts in the proportion of 4 ball to 1 tracer. A six barrelled smoke grenade discharger is mounted on each side of the turret for local protection. The gunner, positioned to the right of the main armament, has a periscopic sight of ×10 magnification. The standard sight is gradually being replaced by the Barr and Stroud LF2 laser rangefinder sight which gives instantaneous accurate ranges to well beyond the capacity of the 120mm gun, and will reduce the need for the RMG.

Chieftain's crew of four, commander, loader/operator, gunner and driver, are surrounded by more armour than in any other current MBT. The hull is made of welded rolled homogeneous plate and the turret has a cast nose and welded rear. The shape of the turret front presents the smallest possible target and the best ballistic protection. The need for a low silhouette called for reduced hull height, so the driver in Chieftain, seated centrally in the hull, adopts a prone position when closed down. His vision is then through a single wide angle periscope, and the driving controls are

designed so as to be used equally well in both the closed down and 'head out' positions.

Chieftain is powered by the Leyland L60 six-cylinder vertically-opposed piston compression-ignition engine. It was designed to use a variety of fuels, from 80 octane gasoline to diesel oil, but it works best on straight diesel. The layout is adapted from the Junkers Jumo aircraft diesel engine of the late 1930s, which in theory gives a high output from a comparatively low weight and volume. It was the low volume that was so attractive to the designers of Chieftain — less weight of armour would be needed to protect the engine compartment, but the closed environment of a tank engine compartment produced problems of heat dispersal from the centre of the engine which took many years to solve.

The 3Kw charging plant which provides power for the radio, gun control equipment etc when the tank's main engine is not running, is also an opposed piston design. It is the three cylinder H30 engine built by Coventry Climax. At the rear of the engine compartment is the TN12 semi-automatic 'hot shift' transmission. It provides 6 forward and 3 reverse ratios, and gear changing is effected by a foot pedal.

Chieftain's running gear and suspension are very similar to those of Centurion, well proven over thirty years. The six road wheels each side are

Left: *The Chieftain bridgelayer in action.* / MOD

Below: *Maintenance on Chieftains after Battle Group training in Canada. Radiators are swung open to allow access to the engine compartments. In winter these workshops are fully heated throughout.* / Robin Adshead

mounted on Horstmann bogies. During comparison trials with the M60 for a foreign customer Chieftain crews experienced a far better cross-country ride over all types of going than M60 crews.

Chieftain has been through many modifications and improvements since its inception. The latest additional equipment is the fitting of a dozer blade to the front of the tank to enable it to dig its own fire positions. The Chieftain ARV FV4203 with dozer blade and heavy recovery should be in service in 1976.

FV4205 Chieftain Bridgelayer
The Chieftain hull has been adapted to carry two types of bridge. With the turret removed and blanked off, the hull is fitted with a launching structure at the front to which the toe of the bridge is attached. Inside the hull are hydraulic pumps, driven from the main engine, which provide the power to launch and recover the bridges. The bridgelayer has a crew of three; laying can be accomplished from under armour but recovery of the bridges necessitates one man dismounting to reconnect the equipment.

The No 8 Tank Bridge is of the scissors type, hinged in the middle and unfolding as it is laid. The bridge weighs 12 tons and is 80ft (24·4m) long, enabling it to bridge a gap up to 75ft (22·8m) in a clear span. The bridge is made up of two tracks each 5ft 4in (1·62m) wide, with a gap of 2ft 6in (0·76m) between the tracks. It is a Class 60 bridge, able to carry all types of vehicles including MBTs.

The alternative bridge is the No 9 Tank Bridge, consisting of a single span 44ft (13·4m) in length. The width and the arrangement of the tracks is the same as for the No 8 bridge, and it is also a Class 60 bridge. It can span a gap of 40ft (12·2m). Both types of bridge can be laid in under five minutes.

Centurion
Main Battle Tank

Vehicle: Centurion Mk 5/2
Crew: 4
Dimensions:
length 9·854m (gun forward) 7·823m (hull)
width 3·39m
height 3·00m
weight 51 820kg
Armament:
main 1 × 105mm L7A2 gun
ammuntion 64 rounds
secondary 1 × 7·62mm coaxial machinegun
and 1 × 7·62mm machinegun on cupola
ammuntion 4 250 rounds
Mobility:
speed (ground) 35kph
range 190km
ground pressure ·95kg/cm²

Although the Centurion was originally designed at the end of WW II it has proved capable of development over the last 30 years so that it is still in service with the Canadian Army, and indeed has only recently been phased out of service with the forces of Britain, Denmark and the Netherlands. It is still a potent weapon in many armies outside NATO and some of its variants are still serving in NATO.

Armed at first with the 17pdr gun, Centurion was soon up-gunned with the 20-pdr, and later with the 105mm L7 gun which has armed the M60, Leopard, Swedish S-Tank, Japanese STB and the Swiss Panzer 61 and Panzer 68. In its final form, with the 105mm gun, ranging machine-gun and coaxial machinegun, Centurion has fire-power comparable to most modern MBTs.

Centurion was built to the British concept of giving maximum protection and the avoidance of damage caused by hits, rather than by using mobility to reduce hits. With its heavy armour it weighs 54 tons and has a maximum road speed of

22mph. The engine is the same Rolls-Royce Meteor petrol engine (developed from the Merlin of WW II aircraft fame) that powered the Cromwell and Comet. It produces 650bhp at 2 550rpm, but fuel consumption is high, and even with improvements to fuel capacity only 80 to 90 miles range could be achieved.

The Horstmann type suspension, with three double bogies each side of the hull, gives very good cross-country performance and Centurion crews arrive in battle in better condition than many others. The capacity of Centurion to absorb punishment has become legendary among the armies that have used it in battle. Many countries still use Centurion and have thought it cost-effective to embark upon expensive re-engine programmes to improve its performance and range. One such conversion uses the same Continental AVDS 1790 engine that powers the M60; another employs a General Motors diesel.

Compared to the 'hot shift' transmission of the Chieftain, driving Centurion is hard work. The gearbox is an improvement upon the Merritt-Brown box in Cromwell and Comet, giving fixed steering radii according to the gear ratio selected, and a most useful neutral turn facility. In Centurion there are five forward and two reverse ratios, the high reverse being used for getting out of trouble quickly. The change is manual and the clutch is heavy, requiring some skill of the driver to get the best out of his vehicle, but control is positive and a good driver can manoeuvre a Centurion in and out of places that other tanks cannot attempt.

From the Mark 5/2, when the 105mm gun was fitted, Centurion has been modernised with infra-red night fighting equipment. Very much in advance of the M60 and the Leopard, Centurion was fitted with fully stabilised main armament from the start. The sight of a Centurion going cross-country with its gun held steadily on target as it manoeuvred to and fro has resulted in many sales to foreign customers, and it was no accident that British units equipped with Centurions held the NATO tank gunnery trophy for many years.

Centurion carries 64 rounds of ammunition for the 105mm gun. The APDS round has a muzzle velocity of 4 700ft/sec (1 450m/sec) and has proved equal to penetrating not only the standard NATO triple test target, but the armour of Russian T54, T55 and T62 tanks, and American M48s. No one has yet tried a Centurion against Leopard or M60, but the results would be similar, at least in penetration effect. The HESH round is particularly effective against well-sloped or curved armour, but its lower velocity, while it causes less barrel wear, necessitates a higher trajectory and therefore greater accuracy in range-taking to achieve a first round hit.

A rate of fire of eight rounds a minute can be achieved by a good crew, and even without the aids of laser rangefinders or the slower optical rangefinders, accuracy has been proved in battle.

Centurion ARV at Suffield training area in Canada. / Robin Adshead

The Indian Army used Centurion Mk 5s with 20pdr guns very successfully against the Pakistanis armed with M47s and Chinese T59s. Many troops asked to be allowed to retain their old Centurions when told that they were to be issued with the new Vickers Vijayanta. In the fighting on the Golan Heights in the October War of 1973, it was the Israeli Centurions that smashed the Syrian attack by T55s and T62s, taking tremendous punishment, but proving capable of taking on, and beating, the best that was thrown against them.

Centurion has been developed into many variants which still remain in service.

Left: Centurion bridgelayers will gradually be replaced by Chieftains. / Robin Adshead

Below: Centurion ARV Mk 2. Its only armament is the pintle-mounted ·30 Browning machinegun at the commander's cupola. Its main equipment is the winch (90 000kg max) and rear spade. / Robin Adshead

Centurion ARV
The Armoured Recovery Vehicle has no turret, but an armoured box superstructure covering the recovery winch, a spade at the rear to improve its pulling capacity with the winch, and a jib which can be raised to act as a crane for lifting engines and gearboxes.

Centurion BARV
The Beach Armoured Recovery Vehicle is the same type of vehicle, but with a much higher superstructure to enable it to operate in 9ft of water.

Centurion AVRE
The Armoured Vehicle Royal Engineers is the descendant of the Churchill AVRE of WWII and is similarly fitted with a 165mm demolition charge projector on the spigot mortar principle for use against concrete bunkers at short ranges, a fascine on the front to fill obstacles and can tow the Giant Viper mine-clearing device. It is fitted with an hydraulically operated dozer blade.

Centurion Bridgelayer
The Centurion Bridgelayer carries a single span bridge for crossing gaps up to 45ft wide. This can be laid in under two minutes. The Netherlands Army still uses Centurions fitted with a scissors bridge.

Saladin
Armoured Car

Vehicle: FV601 (C) Saladin Mk 2
Crew: 3
Dimensions:
length 5·284m (gun forward) 4·93m (hull)
width 2·54m
height 2·39m
weight 11 590kg
Armament:
main 1 ×76mm gun
ammunition 43 rounds
secondary 1 ×7·62mm coaxial machinegun and 1 ×7·62mm machinegun pintle-mounted on roof
ammunition 2 750 rounds
Mobility:
speed (ground) 72kph
range 400km
ground pressure 1·12kg/cm^2

Although design of the Saladin started in 1947, before the Saracen APC, the latter was given priority and it was not until 1954 that the first Saladin prototype was built. Production was from 1958 to 1972, and although Saladin was used by some 20 countries, only Britain and Portugal among NATO Armies, and the West German Border Police, took them into service.

Saladin carries considerable firepower for a wheeled reconnaissance vehicle. The two-man turret mounts a 76mm gun and a coaxial ·30in machinegun, and a second machinegun can be pintle-mounted on the turret roof by the commander's hatch. Multi-barrelled smoke grenade dischargers are carried each side of the turret for local protection. The 76mm gun fires HE, HESH, smoke and canister, and 42 rounds are stowed. Maximum range is 5 500 metres and sighting is by a ×6 periscopic sight in the turret roof.

The mechanical components of Saladin are the same as those of Saracen, except the brakes which are of disc type. The Rolls-Royce B80 engine is mounted at the rear of the hull and the driver is seated centrally at the front. The most noticeable mechanical difference between Saladin and Saracen is in the controls; the Saladin driver pushes the transfer lever in the natural direction of travel, forwards to go forward and back to go in reverse. The Saracen driver, however, sits facing the engine which is in the front of the hull, and has to remember to push the transfer lever backwards to go forwards and vice versa.

Transmission is by propellor shaft to bevel boxes at each wheel station, thus the three wheels on each side are effectively locked together. There is differential action between the two sets of wheels, but despite requests from some users, no lockable differential was provided. This meant that, although it was a rare occurrence it was possible for all the wheels on one side to slip and to take all the drive from the other side. The suspension, by longitudinal torsion bars to double wishbones, gives an excellent cross-country ride and a quick recovery time to settle after firing the gun.

The engine develops 165bhp, which gives a power/weight ratio of only 15bhp/ton. This means that Saladin is under-powered by modern standards, and with the entry into service of the Scorpion CVR(T), Saladin has been relegated to reserve and Internal security duties.

Left: *FV601 Saladin armoured car in British service.* / Christopher Foss

Below: *Saladins on training in England. The ·30 Browning machinegun on the turret roof is used by the vehicle commander.*

Scorpion
Fire Support Vehicle

Vehicle: FV101 Scorpion
Crew: 3
Dimensions:
length 4·388m
width 2·184m
height 2·096m
weight 7 960kg
Armament:
main 1 × 76mm
ammunition 40 rounds
secondary 1 × 7·62mm coaxial machinegun
ammunition 3 000 rounds
Mobility:
speed (ground) 87kph
(water) 6·5kph
range 644km
ground pressure ·35kg/cm^2

The shift of emphasis to the European theatre in the 1960s led the British Army to reconsider its traditional reliance on wheeled AFVs for reconnaissance. It was decided to develop tracked vehicles for the future, though the requirements of silence, speed and reliability were to be as good as, if not an improvement upon those of wheeled vehicles. A great many roles were to be carried out, more than a single type could manage, so a family of vehicles based on common mechanical components was developed by MVEE at Chobham, and Alvis Ltd, builders of the highly successful wheeled vehicles, was made design parents for the family. Development work started in the late 1950s, and the first prototypes were delivered in 1968. Alvis were awarded a production contract for the British Army in 1970, and in 1971 joined in a co-production programme for the Belgian Army.

The basic vehicle of the family is Scorpion, designed to carry out fighting reconnaissance and fire support tasks, and having a good anti-tank capability. It is airportable in the C130 Hercules and can be dropped by parachute or lifted by helicopter. In order to achieve this the battle weight has been kept under 8 tons. The use of aluminium alloy armour has made possible a considerable weight saving, yet still provides better immunity than any other vehicle in its class.

The layout of Scorpion was adopted so as to keep changes in the rest of the family to a minimum. The transmission is forward of the driver, who sits in the front left, with the engine to his right. The two-man fighting compartment is behind the driver, with the fuel tank and NBC pack in the rear of the hull.

Scorpion mounts a 76mm gun in the 360° traverse, low-profile turret, with a 7·62mm GPMG mounted coaxially. This can be used as a ranging machinegun. The 76mm is a lightened and updated version of the weapon in the Saladin armoured car, and fires the same ammunition. Elevation is from −10° to +35° which gives a maximum range of nearly 6 000 metres. The main armament ammunition, of which 40 rounds can be stowed, includes conventional HE, base ejection smoke, HESH and canister. Two multi-barrelled smoke grenade dischargers are fitted, one each side of the turret, for local protection.

The HESH round has an excellent performance against AFVs, enabling Scorpion to kill or disable all known tanks, while its effect against buildings or concrete emplacements is shattering. The canister round was developed to deal with mass attacks as experienced in Korea and is particularly useful in ambush situations. It can be compared to a large scale sawn-off shotgun, scattering its charge of pellets in a wide arc from the muzzle.

The Scorpion is powered by a militarised version of the Jaguar 4·2 litre engine, derated to 195bhp to accept military fuels. This gives the very high power/weight ratio of 25bhp per ton. The engine drives through a centrifugal multi-plate clutch to the transversely mounted gearbox and steering unit. This is a 'hot shift' epicyclic gearbox operated by a foot pedal, giving seven speeds in each direction, controlled by a forward/reverse lever. Top speed is over 50mph, making Scorpion the fastest tracked AFV in service anywhere. Steering is by two conventional levers and provides fixed turning radii according to the gear selected, and a neutral turn. The steering and main brakes are disc type, with a rim brake for parking.

Engine cooling air is drawn in through louvres over the transmission by a mixed flow fan, through the radiator which is horizontal over the transmission, and thence over the engine and out through rear louvres, cooling the exhaust. From the gearbox the drive goes to the front sprockets and the tracks, which are of the single horn type. To keep the noise level low the tracks have rubber pads on the outside and a rubber wheel path on the inside, on which run the rubber tyred road wheels. Much of the noise of a tracked vehicle is from the

A Scorpion rocks on its suspension at the moment of firing its 76mm gun. / Robin Adshead

contact between track links and the sprocket, and in order to minimise this the sprocket has two neoprene rings which take the weight of the track. Suspension is by transverse torsion bars within the hull and there are dampers on front and rear wheel stations. Track adjustment is by an hydraulic ram on the rear idler.

Each vehicle is fitted with a swimming screen which can be erected swiftly by the crew, making Scorpion capable of swimming by track propulsion at about 3mph. For special water crossing operations a propellor kit can be fitted to the sprockets, increasing water speed to 6mph. Scorpion's low ground pressure of only 5lb/sq in gives superb mobility over mud, marsh and soft sand.

Essentially a reconnaissance vehicle, Scorpion is well provided with observation devices. The

Left: Scorpion at speed in Canadian snow trials.

Below: Scorpion on driving instruction. The hydraulic ram of the track tensioner can just be seen in front of the rear idler. / Alvis

turret is equipped with ×10 periscopic sights for commander and gunner, and nine ×1 episcopes for all round observation. The driver has a periscope for closed down operation. Infra-red masks can be fitted to the headlamps for night driving, and a passive image intensifier night sight is mounted in an armoured housing to the right of the gun. An NBC pack is fitted in the rear of the hull.

Scorpion entered service with the British and Belgian armies in 1972, and was subsequently sold to the United Arab Emirates, Nigeria and Iran. There is no doubt that, had it been possible to fit a diesel engine in place of the Jaguar petrol engine, Scorpion would have been acceptable to a wider market. However, at the time when the vehicle was conceived, Britain was still committed to the Far East where the distance between rubber trees in plantations meant a maximum width of 7ft 2in to enable the vehicle to manoeuvre. By the time Scorpion came into service, Britain had withdrawn from the Far East, but the vehicle dimensions were fixed, and there was not room to install a suitable diesel engine. In any case, Scorpion was designed to a stringent weight limit to enable this to be carried in a C130. A diesel engine would carry a weight penalty, but would probably have led to greater sales to foreign armies.

Striker
Anti-Tank Missile Vehicle

In service with the British and Belgian armies, Striker gives the most potent anti-tank defence capability in NATO out to a range of 4 000 metres. Five BAC Swingfire guided missiles are carried in an armoured launcher on the top of the hull, and a further reload is stowed inside. Local protection is by a GPMG mounted on the commander's cupola and twin multi-barrelled smoke grenade dischargers on the hull.

The mechanical components are the same as those of Scorpion, and give a comparable performance on the ground and in water. The missile controller can sight from a position under armour to the right of the commander, or from a separated sight up to 100 metres from the launcher vehicle. Missiles can be launched from behind cover at angles up to 55° from the line of sight to the target. For target illumination at night two Lyran flare launchers are fitted, for which 18 flares are stowed internally. Under the new 'restructured' organisation Striker will be operated by the Royal Artillery.

Vehicle: FV102 Striker
Crew: 3
Dimensions:
length 4·759m
width 2·184m
height 2·210m
weight 8 221kg
Armament:
main Swingfire ATGW
ammunition 10 Missiles
secondary: 1 × 6·72mm machinegun on cupola
ammunition 3 000 rounds
Mobility:
speed (ground) 87kph
  (water) 6·5kph
range 644km
ground pressure ·35kg/cm2

Left: *Striker can fire its missiles from behind cover; the propulsive gases of the Swingfire motors are deflected upwards by the louvres seen at the rear of the missile ramp.* / MOD

Below: *Striker with launching ramp raised and a dummy Swingfire missile emerging. The guidance periscope can be covered by an armoured flap. New, four-barrelled, smoke grenade dischargers are fitted.* / Simon Dunstan

Spartan
Armoured Personnel Carrier

Not to be confused with the FV432 or M113 type of APC, the Spartan is designed to carry an infantry element of the reconnaissance unit. The box-shaped hull has a large rear door for access, and folding roof hatches from which the infantry can fire their personal weapons.

Spartan carries, in addition to the crew of two (commander and driver) a section of five infantry and a store of mines and explosives. For surveillance duties the ZB298 radar can be mounted on the roof. The commander can load and fire the 7·62mm GPMG on his cupola from under armour.

The mechanical components of Spartan are the same as for the rest of the family, and a swimming screen is provided. The vehicle can be sealed for NBC conditions. Spartan can also be used to carry a quantity of shoulder-fired Blowpipe anti-aircraft guided missiles.

Vehicle: FV103 Spartan
Crew: 2 + section of 5
Dimensions:
length   4·839m
width   2·184m
height   2·250m
weight   8·172kg
Armament:
main   1 × 7·62mm machinegun on cupola
ammunition   2 000 rounds
Mobility:
speed (ground)   87kph
   (water)   6·5kph
range   644km
ground pressure   ·35kg/cm^2

Left: *Spartan carries two crew and five infantry, together with all their kit and weapons.* / MOD

Below: *The shape of the commander's hatch is clearly seen in this shot of Spartan, also the 7·62mm general purpose machinegun on the cupola. The three-point mounting behind the cupola is for the ZB298 surveillance radar.*

Samaritan
Armoured
Ambulance

In order to allow the four stretcher patients to be carried in Samaritan the roof height has been raised and a larger rear door fitted. Alternative loads are two stretcher cases and three sitting casualties or six seated, in addition to the crew of two, driver and commander/medical orderly.

Although the commander's hatch is surrounded by a ring of five periscopes, like the cupola of Spartan, no provision is made for any weapon mounting, Samaritan relying for protection on its mobility, armour and local smoke from the hull-mounted dischargers.

Vehicle: FV104 Samaritan
Crew: 2+4 stretcher cases or 6 walking wounded
Dimensions:
length 4·991m
width 2·184m
height 2·016m
weight 7 710kg
Armament:
none
Mobility:
speed (ground) 87kph
  (water) 6·5kph
range 644km
ground pressure ·35kg/cm^2

Left: *The longer hull of Samaritan shows the noticeable gap either side of the centre road wheel.* / MOD

Below: *This side view of Samaritan shows the extra height of the hull necessary to accommodate four stretcher cases. Additional stowage is provided in front of and behind the commander's hatch.*

Sultan
Command Vehicle

Sultan is not intended to compete with the FV432 series Command Vehicle since it cannot provide the same accommodation, but to act as Command Vehicle for units equipped with the Scorpion family of vehicles. The hull is built up to the same height as that of Samaritan and has the same large rear door. The commander's cupola has an external mounting for a 7·62mm GPMG, and large additional stowage bins are carried on the roof.

The internal space is used for additional signal batteries and radio sets, mapboards and seats for the crew of five, including the driver. Fixed to the rear of the hull is an extendable penthouse tent to provide additional accommodation when the vehicle is stationary for long periods.

Vehicle: FV105 Sultan
Crew: 5–6
Dimensions:
length 4·991m
width 2·184m
height 2·016m
weight 7 918kg
Armament:
main 1 × 7·62mm machinegun pintle-mounted on cupola
ammunition 2 000 rounds
Mobility:
speed (ground) 87kph
  (water) 6·5kph
range 644km
ground pressure ·35kg/cm^2

Left: *The raised hull of Sultan and the wider gaps on either side of the centre road wheel clearly indicate the extra size needed for the command vehicle.* / MOD

Below: *The folded 'penthouse' tent at the rear of the Sultan command vehicle extends to give extra accommodation. The hull is longer than that of Scorpion and the gap each side of the centre road wheel shows the extension.* / Simon Dunstan

Samson
Recovery Vehicle

Vehicle: FV106 Samson
Crew: 3
Dimensions:
length 4·934m
width 2·184m
height 2·023m
weight 8 002kg
Armament:
main 1 × 7·62mm machinegun pintle-mounted
ammunition 2 000 rounds
Mobility:
speed (ground) 87kph
(water) 6·5kph
range 644km
ground pressure ·35kg/cm²

Intended to recover vehicles of the Scorpion family (and lighter equipments), Samson is fitted with a Plumett capstan type winch driven from the main engine. The winch has a maximum line pull

of 20 000kg and the capstan stores 229 metres of wire rope, which is fed out over a guide roller at the rear of the hull. A large spade anchor is fitted to enable the winch to be used at full load.

The remainder of the internal space is taken up with stowage for the specialised recovery equipment and tools with which Samson is well provided. The crew consists of driver and commander and one or two recovery fitters. The commander has a cupola with a pintle-mounted machinegun, and there is a smaller hatch to his right and large folding roof hatches as in Spartan. Like all the Scorpion family of vehicles, Samson is fitted with a collapsible floatation screen, and can swim by track propulsion. However, since Samson is intended to take the lead at water crossings and to help other vehicles out of difficult exits with its winch, it is likely to be equipped with the add-on propellor kit which has been developed to improve the swimming speed of the family. The kit, which fits all vehicles in the series, is attached to the front driving sprockets each side.

Left: *Samson, the recovery vehicle of the Scorpion family, winching a FV434 out of trouble. The winch rope is led out of the top of the hull through a guide visible by the warning light. The spade is lowered to an almost vertical position, lifting the rear of Samson.* / MOD

Below: *Samson armoured recovery vehicle. The recovery winch fitted inside the hull is driven from the main engine. Maximum pull is 12 tons.* / Alvis

Scimitar
Reconnaissance Vehicle

To provide an anti-APC capability, without using the 'overkill' of 120mm or 76mm rounds, Scimitar is armed with a 30mm Rarden cannon in a turret similar to that of Scorpion.

The Rarden cannon fires all the standard range of Hispano-Suiza 30mm ammunition and, in addition, specially developed APDS and AP Special Effect rounds. It can penetrate all known light armoured vehicles and the sides and rear of all MBTs up to a range of 1 000 metres. 165 rounds of 30mm ammunition are carried, and 3 000 rounds for the coaxial GPMG.

Vehicle: FV107 Scimitar
Crew: 3
Dimensions:
length 4·388m
width 2·184m
height 2·115m
weight 7 900kg
Armament:
main 1 × 30mm Rarden Cannon
ammunition 165 rounds
secondary 7·62mm coaxial machinegun
ammunition 3 000 rounds
Mobility:
speed (ground) 87kph
(water) 6·5kph
range 644km
ground pressure ·35kg/cm2

Left: *Scimitar's Rarden cannon can kill all types of APC.* / MOD

Below: *Scimitar camouflaged in white and dark green.* / MOD

Fox
Armoured Car

Vehicle: FV721 Fox
Crew: 3
Dimensions:
length 5·359m (gun forward) 4·242m (hull)
width 2·134m
height 2·20m (overall) 1·98m (turret top)
weight 5 670kg
Armament:
main 1 ×30mm Rarden Cannon
ammunition 96 rounds
secondary 1 ×7·62mm coaxial machinegun
ammunition 2 600 rounds
Mobility:
speed (ground) 104kph
 (water) 6kph
range 434km
ground pressure ·46kg/cm^2

The family of Combat Vehicles, Reconnaissance, was conceived in 1965, to replace the existing Ferret, Saladin and Saracen. It was decided that, although the reconnaissance elements of the Divisions of BAOR would be on tracks, it was necessary to retain a wheeled element for long range road work, liaison and Internal Security roles for which tracked vehicles would be inappropriate.

The Daimler Company, whose development of the Dingo and Ferret Scout Cars gave them good background experience, was awarded a research and development contract for the new wheeled vehicles. The first prototype was built in under two years, followed over a period by 16 more, in which all the new components and ideas were tested. Unfortunately for Daimler, the production contract that resulted was awarded to the Royal Ordnance Factory at Leeds, despite the fact that the ROF had no experience of wheeled vehicles, and that the engine, transmission and turret of Fox all came from within the British Leyland group to which Daimler belong.

The hull and turret of Fox are made of alumin-

Left: The armoured casing seen to the right of the Rarden 30mm cannon is for the Rank passive night sight on Fox. / Robin Adshead

ium armour, well angled for ballistic protection. A floatation screen is fitted to the top line of the hull, giving Fox sufficient buoyancy to swim by wheel propulsion at about 4mph. The driver has a reverse-angled steering wheel and controls similar to those of Ferret, but in Fox power-assisted steering is provided. The pre-selector gearbox, fluid coupling, H-drive and coil spring suspension are also derived from previous Daimler vehicles.

The power unit in Fox is the Jaguar 4·2 litre, six-cylinder petrol engine, first used in the Jaguar XK series of sports cars, which is common to all the vehicles of the CVR family, including the tracked versions made by Alvis. In the civil version the engine produced 265bhp, but in CVR it has a reduced compression ratio to enable it to burn military gasoline, and develops 195bhp.

Fox is armed with the Rarden 30mm cannon and a coaxial 7·62mm GPMG, and a four-barrelled smoke grenade discharger is mounted at each side of the curved turret. The Rarden cannon was designed so as to take up the minimum space in the turret and has an inboard length of less than ten inches. Nevertheless, the two-man turret of Fox seems very cramped when occupied.

The Rarden barrel is supported externally for almost half its length to damp vibrations. The gun fires all the standard Hispano-Suiza 30mm AP and HE rounds and also British designed APDS and APSE (Armour Piercing Special Effects) rounds. A total of 96 rounds is stowed in clips of three and six rounds at a time can be loaded into the cannon. The Rarden normally fires single rounds, but has the ability to fire six-round bursts at the rate of about 90 rounds per minute. The spent cases are ejected forwards out of the turret, as are the GPMG cases, which reduces the escape of gases into the turret. The gun elevates to 40° at which angle it can give deterrent fire against helicopters, but has no real anti-aircraft capability.

Fox is a reconnaissance vehicle and is very well equipped with observation and surveillance devices. The commander, seated on the left of the rather cramped turret, has a periscope binocular and seven episcopes for all round vision. The gunner has a periscopic binocular sight and two episcopes, as well as a passive image intensification night sight mounted in an armoured housing on the mantlet to the right of the gun barrel.

In the surveillance role a ZB298 Radar can be carried on the turret, and radiation detection and gas alarms can be fitted. No spare wheel is carried, since the tyres are Run Flat, and give 50 miles running even when fully deflated.

Although the first production unit came off the line in May 1973, not enough Fox have been made to replace Ferret in Reconnaissance units. The sister vehicle, Vixen FV722, which was to have taken over the liaison role was cancelled as a result of defence cuts in 1972, and Fox is therefore the only wheeled AFV in production in Great Britain.

Ferret
Scout Car

Vehicle: FV701 Ferret Mk 2/3
Crew: 2
Dimensions:
length 3·84m
width 1·91m
height 1·88m
weight 4 395kg
Armament:
main 1 × 7·62mm machinegun
ammunition 2 500 rounds
Mobility:
speed (ground) 93kph
range 300km

Built by the Daimler Co, the Ferret Scout Car owes much to its ancestor the famous Daimler Dingo. The basic mechanical layout is the same: rear engine, fluid flywheel, preselector gearbox, transfer box and shaft drive to each independently sprung wheel. The transfer box permits using the five gearbox ratios in each direction — forward and reverse. The driver sits centrally in front of and below the commander and can see through three large vision flaps or through the periscopes mounted in them. The Ferret Mk 1 is an open-topped liaison vehicle with a 7·62mm GPMG on a pintle mounting to his front. Two 3-barrelled smoke grenade dischargers are carried on the front wings. The radio equipment is mounted behind the commander's seat, rather awkward to reach and vulnerable to a steel shod boot when standing or entering or leaving the vehicle.

The Mk 2/3, designated Scout Car Reconnaissance, has a manually operated turret mounting a ·30in Browning machinegun or a GPMG. It can be closed down for protection against small arms, airburst and splinters. Sighting is through a ×1 periscope with a simple graticule, and aiming by a shoulder pad on the gun mounting and on the turret ring. Mechanically the Mk 2/3 is identical to the Mk 1 and also to the Mk 2/6, which is merely a Mk 2/3 with two Vigilant ATGW launchers mounted either side of the turret and stowage for two more missiles on the left hand side of the vehicle in place of the spare wheel. The machinegun is retained, and the missiles can be fired and controlled by the commander from inside the turret or from a separated firing position up to 50 metres from the vehicle, by using a combined sight/controller and separation cable.

Although the cross-country performance of the Mk 1 and Mk 2 Ferrets was good, it was felt that improvements could be made to give a better ride for the commander, who, over rough going, had to cling like a limpet. The Mk 4 (FV711) version was provided with stronger suspension units, disc brakes and 11·00 × 20 rm flat tyres in place of the 9·00 × 16 RF of the earlier model. This necessitated slight changes to the mudguards and stowage bins and resulted in a cleaner line. Mechanical and interior details remained virtually unchanged.

The Ferret Mk 5, which was produced in a very small series, is basically identical to the Mk 4 with the exception of the turret. This mark carries the larger Swingfire ATGW and to accommodate the missiles and controller's sight a wide flat turret was designed with four missiles carried in two twin launchers which could be raised to an angle of about 40° for firing. Two spare missiles are stowed in armoured boxes, one on each side of the hull. The machinegun is retained, mounted to the left of the commander and aimed and fired as before.

With the development of the Mk 4 'Big-Wheeled' Ferret, the opportunity was taken to make the Ferret swim. Modifications were tried out to all marks, by fitting a collapsible floatation screen round the outside of the hull and mudguards, propulsion in the water being by rotation of the vehicle wheels giving a speed of 2–3mph.

Ferret has been in service since 1951, and since the cancellation of the new FV722 Vixen in 1974 it appears that it may continue for many more years. While some two thousand Ferrets have been sold overseas only Britain and Canada in NATO have them in service.

Left: *Ferret Mk 2/3 on duty in Cyprus.* / Robin Adshead

Below: *Ferret Mk 2/6 with BAC Vigilant first generation ATGWs each side of the turret which also mounts a ·30 Browning machinegun. The armoured box on the rear wing contains the radio aerial tuning device which has to be moved out to make room for missile guidance in the hull.* / RAC Centre

FV432
Armoured Personnel Carrier

Vehicle: FV432
Crew: 12
Dimensions:
length 5·251m
width 2·80m
height 2·286m (including machinegun) 1·879m
(hull)
weight 15 280kg
Armament:
main 1 × 7·62mm machinegun
ammunition 2 750 rounds
Mobility:
speed (ground) 52kph
(water) 6·6kph
range 580km
ground pressure ·78kg/cm²

FV432 is unique among British armoured vehicles in having no name, but a number. All AFVs have numbers, of course, but somehow Trojan, the name by which the original FV432 was known has been discontinued. The 432 series of vehicles is descended from the well-known carriers of WWII, via the Oxford and Cambridge carriers of the immediate postwar years, and the largely experimental FV500, FV300 and FV420 families. The experience on these provided a firm basis for the work on the FV432, the first of which saw the light in 1961.

Produced by GKN Sankey Ltd, the FV432 series of vehicles has run to almost as many variants as the very similar M113, but since it is used only by the British Army, the production run has been very much smaller. The original concept was very much the same as the M113, but the British vehicle is built of steel armour and does not have the inherent buoyancy of the M113.

FV432 carries a crew of two, driver and commander, and a section of 10 infantrymen in the rear compartment. The driver, seated at the right hand side front of the vehicle, with the com-

FV432 with Wombat 120mm recoilless rifle; on top of the Wombat is seen the ·5 inch ranging gun. / Robin Adshead

mander behind him, has the engine compartment immediately to his left. The Rolls-Royce K60 engine is a scaled down version of the L60 which powers Chieftain, and is a six-cylinder, vertically opposed piston unit which can run on a variety of fuels, from diesel, through aviation kerosene and JP4 to ordinary 80 octane army petrol, but it is happiest and most economical on diesel. The power pack is accessible through the louvred hatches immediately above, and can be lifted out complete on its own sub-frame, still connected to the vehicle systems by long leads which enable it to be test run outside the hull. Across the width of the hull in front of the driver's feet is the steering and final drive unit, which transmits power from the Allison 6-speed semi-automatic transmission to the sprockets.

The five road wheels each side are rubber tyred, and mounted on torsion bar suspension. The manganese track plates are rubber padded and rubber bushed. Track tension is maintained by an hydraulic tensioner.

The crew compartment in the rear of the vehicle has longitudinal seats for the section of infantry that is the normal load. Access is by a single large door in the rear, and in the roof is a circular hatch which can be folded back to allow some of the infantry to fire their personal weapons from a head-and-shoulders out position. As in the original M113, no provision has been made for firing ports. In the original model and many of the production vehicles the engine exhaust leaves the side of the hull at the engine compartment, and reaches to the rear of the hull. However, on some standard APC vehicles, and on many of the variants, the exhaust is taken from the roof of the hull, just behind the louvres from which the cooling air emerges, and the exhaust pipe runs along the top of the hull to just behind the roof hatch. This means that when the hatch is open, as in warm climates it would probably be, the men in the rear compartment are subjected to the hot air from the engine and the heat of the exhaust system, and if the wind is in the wrong direction when the vehicle is halted, to exhaust fumes as well. Although the exhaust pipe on the roof is partly covered by a steel shield, enough hot pipe is available to cause unpleasant burns to the unwary.

FV432 is not the noisiest of AFVs, but the crew of a tank, and the driver and commander of the 432, usually wear headsets which alleviate the engine roar, transmission whine and track rattle. The infantry section travelling in an FV432 have no headsets, and a few hours on the move, closed down, can be unpleasant enough to make disembarking a pleasure, even in the worst of weather. However, it is better than walking.

The commander of the FV432 has a GPMG for protection or covering fire, but since it is mounted outside his cupola, he has to fire from an exposed position. For local smoke protection, two multi-barrelled smoke grenade projectors are fitted to the

glacis plate, on either side of the large hatch which gives access to the transmission. This hatch is usually obscured by the adjustable trimming board which is angled forward when the vehicle is swimming, to prevent the pressure of water on the glacis plate pushing the bows under. Floatation is achieved by erecting a buoyancy screen which is permanently attached round the top of the hull, and 432 can move at about 4mph in still waters, propelled by its tracks.

The many variants in service with the British Army are:

Carl-Gustav: with the weapon mounted on a bar across the main hatch.

Mortar: with 81mm mortar on 360° traverse mounting and 160 bombs.

Wombat: with Wombat 120mm anti-tank recoilless gun mounted above the hull on a sliding mount to enable the venturi to project over the rear of the hull for firing. Twelve rounds of Wombat ammunition are stowed.

Command Post and Penthouse: fitted with mapboards on either side and tables, with a central seat; extra lighting and stowage and provision for additional radio equipment. The Penthouse is an extendable tent which is carried folded onto the rear of the hull; this provides extra space for the Command Post, and is fitted with additional lighting.

Winch and Earth Anchor: when fitted with a Plumett double capstan winch in the hull, and an earth anchor at the rear, this vehicle is capable of recovering others of the same family (or smaller). The winch is driven from a power take-off on the main engine transfer case, giving a maximum direct pull on the 250 metres of wire rope of 6·5 tons, though this can be tripled by using snatch blocks which are stowed on the vehicle.

Ambulance: provision for four stretcher cases or two stretchers and five seated casualties. In this role no armament is carried.

FV432 is also used to carry many types of equipment for units other than the Infantry. For the Royal Engineers it carries Giant Viper, the minefield clearance device and tows the Bar-Mine Layer, which can lay up to 700 mines an hour. The Royal Artillery use 432 to carry FACE, the Field Artillery Computer Equipment for the Self-Propelled Bat-

teries, and mortar-locating radar and sonic detection equipment. The 432 hull is also the basis of the Abbot 105mm SP gun which is the standard equipment of the Field Regiments.

Experimental versions have been built to carry other weapons such as the 30mm Rarden gun in either the Fox turret or a single man turret, and both Ferret and Saladin turrets have been tried out but not brought into service.

The FV432 family has been extended into other numbered variants. These are:

FV433 the Abbot 105mm Self Propelled Gun.

FV434 Carrier, Maintenance, Full Tracked, fitted with a HIAB hydraulically operated crane with a maximum lift of 3·05 tonnes, carrying REME fitters and their tools and equipment.

FV436 Green Archer Mortar Locating Radar (now being superseded by the Cymbeline equipment).

FV438 the latest of the series, the Swingfire launcher. This variant has a pair of launchers and guidance equipment mounted on the roof of the hull, and 14 spare missiles under armour. Swingfire has a maximum range of 4 000 metres and is capable of killing all known main battle tanks at this range, making FV438 one of the most powerful AFVs for its size.

FV439 a special communications vehicle for the Royal Signals.

The FV432 is used by every type of combat unit in the British Army, except the Airborne. Its boxlike hull, giving protection against small arms fire, blast and splinter, can be sealed against NBC attack. It can be adapted to carry most types of weapons and equipment and is certainly one of the most versatile AFVs in the world. It will certainly continue in British service for many years, and is capable of much role development.

Left: *FV432 with HIAB crane on training in Canada. / Robin Adshead*

Right: *Reconnaissance elements of infantry battalions were to have been equipped with FV432 APCs armed with a Rarden 30mm cannon in a Fox type turret. Defence cuts and 'reorganisation' have removed the recce platoon and the need for this powerful version of the FV432. The height of the turret ring was necessary to allow sufficient depression of the gun.*

Saracen
Armoured Personnel Carrier

Vehicle: FV603 Saracen Mk 2
Crew: 12
Dimensions:
length 4·85m (5·233m with reverse flow cooling modification)
width 2·539m
height 2·463m
weight 10 413kg
Armament:
main 1 × 7·62mm machinegun
ammunition 3 000 rounds
Mobility:
speed (ground) 72kph
range 400km
ground pressure ·98kg/cm^2

Experiences in WWII had shown the British Army the need for an APC, but the only vehicles available at the time were American. Postwar, the Army set to design its own APC, and by 1950 the requirement had been turned into the first prototype. In 1951 the vehicle carried out mobility trials in comparison with the Panhard EBR, against which it showed up a clear winner. Production started at Alvis Ltd in Coventry in 1952, and continued for 20 years, about 2 000 vehicles being supplied to overseas customers. However, only the British Army, among NATO countries, adopted the Saracen. Although it has been superseded by the tracked FV432 for service in Infantry Battalions, it is still in demand for Internal Security roles and reserve units.

The steel monocoque hull carries a crew of two plus a section of 10 fully armed infantry, providing immunity from small arms fire, splinter and blast. The manually operated turret mounts a ·30in Browning machinegun (or a GPMG in later versions) fired by the vehicle commander and aimed through a ×1 periscope sight. A Bren or GPMG can be mounted on a rotating ring at the rear of the roof, and multi-barrelled smoke grenade dischargers are carried on each front mudguard.

Access to the hull is by two large rear doors, and there are eight simple firing ports to enable the infantry to fire their personal weapons from under cover, three each side and two in the rear doors. No vision devices are provided for the infantry, but the driver has three episcopes for use when closed down, and with luck the section commander of the infantry might get a quick look at the situation outside before leaping out into battle.

The Rolls-Royce B80 petrol engine mounted in the front of the hull develops 165bhp, and drives through a fluid flywheel to a five-speed preselector gearbox and a transfer box which gives forward or reverse direction of drive to the propshafts. These take the drive to bevel boxes at each of the six wheel stations, and to the planetary hub reduction final drives. The only differential action is between all the wheels on each side. Each wheel is independently sprung by torsion bars mounted longitudinally outside the hull. Front and rear wheel stations are fitted with telescopic shock absorbers. Tyres are 12·00 × 20 Run Flat, which allow 50 miles running when completely deflated. Even if a wheel is blown off by a mine, Saracen can still get out of trouble on the remaining five.

No air conditioning or NBC equipment is fitted, but fresh air is circulated by fans mounted in armoured housings on the right hand side of the hull, through trunking to aircraft type outlets at each crew position.

The characteristic whine of the transmission can prove trying to the crew when closed down for long periods, but overall Saracen is one of the more comfortable APCs ever built, with a very good cross-country performance.

Left: Saracen FV610 command vehicle with tall hull and additional stowage. / Central Office of Information

Right: Saracen FV604 armoured vehicle for artillery gun position officers. The auxiliary generator on the mudguard is to charge the signal batteries while halted. / MOD

65

Abbot
Self Propelled Gun

Vehicle: FV433 Abbot
Crew: 4
Dimensions:
length 5·84m (gun forward) 5·709m (hull)
width 2·641m
height 2·489m
weight 16 556kg
Armament:
main 1 × 105mm field gun
ammunition 40 rounds
secondary 1 × 7·62mm machinegun on cupola
ammunition 1 200 rounds
Mobility:
speed (ground) 48kph
(water) 5kph
range 390km
ground pressure ·89kg/cm^2

Following the British tradition of giving ecclesiastical names to self-propelled artillery, the new 105mm equipment, which was designed in the late 1960s to replace the ageing 25pdr Sextons, was called Abbot. The requirement was for increased range and lethality in a self-contained and well protected mobile unit. The new gun achieves 40% greater range and 50% greater lethality than its predecessor and is more versatile and more mobile.

Since the requirement for mobility closely paralleled that of the FV432 APC which was under development at the same time, it was natural to utilise as many common components as possible. The power train, suspension and running units of Abbot are the same as those of FV432, but the lower hull height of Abbot, with its better angled glacis plate, necessitated 're-packaging' the K60 engine and auxiliaries. The power packs are not, therefore, interchangeable, though a high proportion of components and spare parts are common to both vehicles.

Abbot is not inherently buoyant, but a collapsible swimming screen is permanently fitted to the top of the hull, and when erected, allows Abbot to swim at about 3mph by means of track propulsion.

The driver sits alongside the engine at the right hand front of the hull, and can operate 'head out' or closed down. The remainder of the crew, commander, layer and loader, are accommodated in the 360° traverse turret at the back of the hull, with access by roof hatches or via the large, square door at the rear, which is the usual access for loading ammunition.

The 105mm gun mounted in the turret can elevate from −5° to +70°. Maximum range is 17 000 metres, and in high angle it can search with fire dead ground down to only 2 500 metres range. Forty rounds of 105mm ammunition can be stowed in and around the turret. These are usually a mixture of HE and HESH, with smoke and illuminating rounds issued as required. The HESH round is capable of knocking out most tanks and is very effective against buildings and strongpoints.

To maintain the high rate of fire demanded, up to 12 rounds a minute, a mechanical rammer is used to load the projectile, but the separate propellant cartridge case is hand loaded. All functions of loading, aiming and firing can be carried out from under armour. When closed down under NBC conditions clean air is provided through a built-in NBC pack. The fume extractor fitted half way along the gun barrel prevents propellant gases entering the turret through the semi-automatic breech, which remains open after firing. The gun barrel has a life of over 10 000 rounds.

For local protection Abbot can mount a 7·62mm GPMG on the commander's cupola and a three-barrelled smoke grenade discharger is fitted each side of the turret.

In NATO only the British Army uses Abbot, but a Value Engineered version has been sold to India, and is also used by British troops training in Canada. The VE Abbot has no swimming screen, mechanical rammer, NBC or smoke dischargers. All NATO forces intend to use the 155mm medium gun as the standard field piece, but until that day comes Britain has one of the best 105mm guns available.

Left: *Value engineered Abbot 105mm SP gun in Canada.* / Robin Adshead

Below: *A troop of Abbot 105mm SP howitzers preparing to fire. Anti-aircraft defence is still provided by the Bren light machinegun, rebored to accept 7·62 × 51mm standard NATO rounds.*

M60
Main Battle Tank

Vehicle: M60A1
Crew: 4
Dimensions:
length 9·436m (gun forward) 6·946 (hull)
width 3·631m
height 3·257m
weight 48 081kg
Armament:
main 1 × 105mm
ammunition 63 rounds
secondary 1 × 7·62mm coaxial machinegun
and 1 × 12·7mm (·50in) on cupola
ammunition 7·62mm – 5 950 rounds, 12·7mm
– 900 rounds
Mobility:
speed (ground) 48kph
range 500km
ground pressure ·79kg/cm²

It became apparent in the mid-1950s that America was slipping behind in the up-gunning race. The 100mm guns of the Soviet T54 and T55 tanks were obviously superior to the 90mm of the M48, and a number of European armies were following the British lead in adopting the 105mm calibre, mostly using the British gun as then fitted to Centurion. The Americans had already proved the weapon and its installation in various versions of the M48, so it was a natural development to install the same gun in the new MBT, the M60, which was first ordered in 1960. The original turret was very like that of the M48, and work started immediately to improve the room in the turret by shifting the trunnions forward. The 'sharp-nosed' effect also greatly enhanced the ballistic protection of the armour. On the original turret the same M1 commander's cupola was used as on the M48, but subsequent marks, from M60A1, had an improved cupola, the M19, still mounting a ·50 calibre machinegun but larger than the M1. This

M60A1 in modern camouflage colours: note the black stars on turret and rear track guards. The eliptical shape of the hull can be clearly seen. / Robin Adshead

brought the overall height of the tank to 10ft 8¼in, making it the tallest MBT in the world.

At the same time as the US Army decided to adopt the British 105mm tank gun, they were developing the Shillelagh gun/missile launcher, and this was to be mounted in a variant of M60 as well as in the M551 Sheridan and the new main battle tank of the 70s (MBT70). The turret for Shillelagh carries the 152mm gun, with the commander directly behind the piece, and the gunner and loader located low on either side of the main armament. The frontal silhouette is therefore reduced except for the commander's cupola. A disadvantage of this design is that the gunner and loader have very limited fields of view and so more observation duty is required of the commander.

Most of the 'bugs' are said to have been removed from the gun/missile system, but the infra-red command link for the missile still remains a detectable source which could alert the intended target, and pinpoint the launcher for counterfire. Despite the size of the ammunition, this version of M60 was able to carry 13 missiles and 33 conventional rounds. It also mounted a 7·62mm coaxial machinegun and a ·50 calibre gun in the cupola.

During the very trying period of testing and improving the Shillelagh system, MBT70, for which Shillelagh was to have been the main armament, was killed off. The Germans dropped it first, realising that, even if it worked, they couldn't afford it. Then, when the projected unit cost rose to over one million dollars, MBT70 was cut from the production programme and relegated in status to that of a design study for the MBT80. This left the American tank force far behind every other major power in the quality of its armour. In the West, Leopard, Chieftain and the French AMX30 were competing for the markets of the non-producing countries, and in the East the threat now included the T62 tank armed with a smoothbore 115mm gun of great potential lethality.

Obviously the existing M60 had to be brought up to as high a standard of battleworthiness as possible, and as soon as possible. Production of Shillelagh turrets was suspended and all available hulls were fitted with 105mm guns.

M60 A1
Modified M60A1 tanks were to become the M60A1E1 in which the original mechanical ballistic computer was replaced by the new solid state electronic computer and fire control system. All new vehicles built to this standard were called M60A1E2 (later M60A3), and included passive night fighting equipment, laser rangefinder, and the electronic fire control system. They were to have been stabilised as well, but the development of the hydraulic stabilisation system brought a new spate of troubles. The turret power traverse also uses hydraulics, and the very high pressures (about 3 000lb/psi) of the system caused serious problems of valve wear, filtration and damage due to

vibration. The dangers of using oil at such high pressures appeared in combat during the October War of 1973 when the Israelis suffered many crew casualties from oil leaks in the turrets of their M60s, following otherwise non-lethal hits on the tank. Stabilisation was eventually introduced as a retrofit AOS (Add on Stabiliser) in 1974, and on subsequent production models M60A3.

Mechanically the M60 follows the pattern established in previous American tanks. The Continental AVDS1790 diesel engine gives far better fuel consumption and range than the gasoline version, and has also been retrofitted to many M48s. The Allison torque converter transmission is virtually the same as in the previous series. The driver's steering control is no longer the steering wheel type, but a form of handlebar, pivoted in the centre, just below the driver's periscope. The torsion bar suspension of the early models is being replaced (and retrofitted) by a tube-over-bar suspension which improves the cross country ride. Despite the attempt to produce something completely new in the MBT70, the Americans seem to

have been pressured by events into a series of improvements on existing designs. The result is that they are going to have in service for a number of years to come, a tank that evolved from a 1944 design. It will have all the modern 'add-on-aids' like laser rangefinder, stabilisation, electronic fire-control system, but the total weapon system which these items make up, on a sound but uninspired hull, is not as battleworthy as that which NATO requires.

The M60 will be replaced eventually by the production version of the XM-1. This will give the American tank force a vehicle equal or superior to those of other nations and capable of extensive development.

M60 AVLB
Another M60 variant is the Armoured Vehicle Launched Bridge which carries the same bridging equipment as the M48 AVLB. The class 60 bridge, which can be laid in two minutes, can span a gap of 18·30 metres.

M728 Combat Engineer Vehicle (CEV)
Based on the M60A1 hull and turret, the CEV mounts a 165mm demolition charge projector, similar to that of the British Centurion AVRE, and the usual 7·62mm coaxial and 12·7mm anti-aircraft machineguns. An hydraulically operated dozer blade is mounted on the nose, and an 'A' frame for lifting. An eleven ton capacity winch is driven from the main engine.

Left: *An early M60A2 armed with the 152mm gun/missile launcher on the range at Grafenwöhr. The loaders hatch behind the Xenon searchlight is open.* / Robin Adshead

Below: *M60 armoured vehicle launched bridge in Germany. The bridge capacity is 60 tons.*

M48
Main Battle Tank

Vehicle: M48A3
Crew: 4
Dimensions:
length 8·686m (gun forward) 6·882m (hull)
width 3·631m
height 3·124m
weight 47 173kg
Armament:
main 1 ×90mm
ammunition 62 rounds
secondary 1 ×7·62mm coaxial and 1 ×12·7mm
on cupola
ammunition 6 000 rounds of 90mm and 630 of
12·7mm
Mobility:
speed (ground) 48kph
range 470km
ground pressure ·83kg/cm^2

The M48 has been in service with six NATO countries and is still the main tank of the Turkish Army, which is the key to the southern flank of NATO. It was developed from the earlier M47 as the result of a rush programme during the Korean War.

When considering the evolution of the American MBT it is useful to start from the M26 Pershing which saw service in small numbers in 1945. This mounted a 90mm gun with coaxial and bow machineguns; turret traverse was hydraulic, and the gun could be stabilised in elevation. The hull and turret were made from homogeneous castings. There were six road wheels each side, rear sprockets driven by an automatic transmission and torsion bar suspension. From the Pershing came the M46 Patton, by the provision of a new engine and transmission and it was on to this hull that a new turret design was added as a temporary measure at the beginning of the Korean war in 1950.

M47 of the Italian army on training exercise. / Stato Maggiore dell'Esercito

The new turret was cast with a long bustle to act as counterweight to the new 90mm gun. The length of the bustle was exaggerated by the addition of a stowage bin of the same section. The new gun had a bore evacuator but no muzzle brake. Across the turret was an optical rangefinder, the optics of which protruded at each side in the form of stubby 'ears'.

The new turret was such an improvement that the hybrid vehicle became standardised as the M47. At the same time, a newly designed hull was built from castings and welded plate, thus M47 hulls could be seen of two types, based on the old M26/M46 and the new genuine M47. Despite the initial troubles with which the M47 was plagued, the type saw service all over the world with 23 countries, and modified and modernised is still on the market today, up-gunned with the ubiquitous British 105mm gun.

All the major components of the M47, engine, transmission, suspension and armament, went straight into the M48. Because of the critical supply situation, production contracts were awarded to Chrysler, Ford and General Motors between 1950 and 1954. It was thought that the tried and tested components being incorporated would produce a good vehicle in short time, but the tests held after the first deliveries in 1952 discovered so many defects that 'initial production vehicles were defective to such an extent that they were not acceptable even for training purposes'.

The Army, however, insisted that the majority of failures were due to poor maintenance, poor driving and improper usage, and it seems a fair assumption that this could be true. But the search for improvement must have contributed to the huge lists of marks, hybrids and variants of which the M48 was the progenitor.

The M48 has an ellipsoid cast hull with very good ballistic properties, and an ellipsoid cast turret. The hull has the driver in a central position and no co-driver or hull gunner, as there was in the M46 and M47.

Early M48s had five return rollers each side above the six road wheels, but from the M48A1E2 the second and fourth return rollers were removed. Suspension is by torsion bar, and track tension is maintained by a small idler just under the sprocket.

The Continental AV 1790 air cooled gasoline engine has gone through many improvements but none have managed to do much for the fuel consumption which limits the range of action, only 70 miles radius in the early vehicles and 160 with larger fuel tanks. Jettison tanks were fitted to some vehicles but are generally considered to be too great a fire hazard. The driver controls the vehicle with a large rectangular steering wheel, the deflection of which regulates the steering brakes of the Allison transmission. The torque convertor stage of the transmission drives through high and low ratios in both forward and reverse directions.

The 90mm gun barrel has a bore evacuator and

a T-shaped muzzle brake. It is mounted with an external shield or mantlet and a ·30in machinegun is mounted coaxially. It fires several natures of ammunition: HE and WP smoke at 2 400fps; HEAT at 2 800fps; AP at 3 050fps; HVAP at 4 050fps. Practice, canister, super-velocity AP and a 'flame thrower' round are also available. Sixty to sixty-four rounds of main armament ammunition are stowed, according to the mark.

The turret has hydraulic power traverse and elevation. The original stereo-rangefinder was replaced by a coincidence type after it was discovered that many men were unable to use stereo optics and were disconnecting the sighting gear. Range data is fed mechanically into the ballistic computer where it is modified by the ammunition and ballistic data selected manually by the gunner and then transmitted to the gunner's periscopic sight.

The commander's cupola rotates through 360°. At the rear is the hatch which hinges back to open. At the front is mounted a ·50in machinegun with elevation from −10° to +60°. The gun is mounted lying on its left side so that it can be loaded from under armour, and is fired by electric solenoid. Five vision blocks are located round the base of the cupola, but they are not much use except for looking into the air, and the commander's periscope sight is a better observation device. The commander does not, in fact, have a very good view from under cover and this may be one cause of high casualties among tank commanders who feel that they must have a good look round the battlefield. It is also questionable whether the ·50 calibre machinegun is a good idea. It may have some slight deterrent effect against aircraft, but precious little chance of a hit, and its very presence tempts the tank commander to do a little (ineffective) shooting on his own account rather than commanding his tank and getting the best out of the main armament. The poor visibility from the cupola was partially cured in some vehicles by interposing a vision block riser between turret and cupola, giving all round observation for the commander, and adding another 8in to the height of the tank.

The M48 has been up-gunned twice, with the British 105mm gun and also with the 152mm Shillelagh gun/missile launcher mounted in a specially designed turret. This had the commander's cupola situated directly behind the gun/launcher, and hatches low down each side of the gun for the gunner and loader. The idea was to reduce the frontal silhouette, but the advantage of the lower sides was nullified by the towering height of the cupola.

M48 AVLB
The M48 Armoured Vehicle Launched Bridge is a conventional type of scissors bridge of Class 60 standard capable of crossing a 50ft gap. The crew of two, driver and commander, can lay and recover the bridge while closed down under armour.

M48 ARV
For tank recovery under fire the M48 was developed into the M88 Armoured Recovery Vehicle. This has a large box-like hull with two driving positions and a commander's cupola of the same M1 type as on the MBT, with a ·50 calibre machinegun. At the front is an hydraulically operated dozer blade, and the recovery winch driven from the main engine can pull from front or rear.

The M48 series of vehicles has been re-designed, re-armed, re-vamped and renovated so much that the variations are almost infinite. It is not the world's greatest tank, but it is certainly one of the most widely used and most versatile. Now that the cost of a new MBT has risen above what most countries can afford, the possibilities of further improvement in power plants, weaponry and fire-control systems on M48s becomes more and more cost effective, and we shall certainly see the M48 and its derivatives in service for some time to come, even though it is being phased out in those countries which have adopted Leopard.

Left: *An M48 of the German army: the can slung on the side of the turret is marked 'III Zug' or 3 Troop.*

Right: *M47s of the Italian army on river crossing manoeuvres.* / Italian MOD

M114
Command and Reconnaissance Vehicle

Vehicle: M114
Crew: 3–4
Dimensions:
length 4·460m
width 2·330m
height 2·310m
weight 6 846kg
Armament:
main 1 × 12·7mm machinegun or 1 × 20mm cannon
ammunition 1 000 and 500 rounds
secondary 1 × 7·62mm machinegun
ammunition 3 000 rounds
Mobility:
speed (ground) 58kph
(water) 5·4kph
range 480km
ground pressure ·35kg/cm²

Developed as part of the long search for a suitable reconnaissance vehicle for the American Army, M114 started in 1956 and was eventually standardised in 1963. The prototypes had a turret-mounted machinegun, but the production versions were provided with hatches for the commander and observer, on which were mounted various combinations of medium and heavy machineguns and, on some variants, a 20mm cannon.

The M114 is built of welded aluminium armour, and weighs only 6 846kg loaded. It is inherently buoyant, and fitted with a trim board on the glacis plate. Under track propulsion it can swim at 5·4kph. It is easily recognisable by its large circular rear door.

Unusually for an American Fighting Vehicle, M114 is powered by a gasoline engine, a V-8 Chevrolet producing 160bhp, which gives the relatively high power/weight ratio of just over 23bhp/ton, but its top speed is only 58kph, compared with Scorpion's 87kph.

Although built as a Command and Reconnaissance vehicle, the M114 is really neither large enough to act as a Command vehicle nor well-endowed with vision devices and sensors to give it a modern reconnaissance capability. In service in Vietnam it showed up many defects, the main one being the necessity for the crew to expose themselves in order to fire their weapons.

M114 will eventually be replaced by whatever the Americans design to fulfill the ARSV (Armoured Reconnaissance Scout Vehicle) role, the search for which has been under way since 1963. After various returns to the drawing board, the latest items offered for consideration were a wheeled vehicle based on the Lockheed Twister and a tracked version from FMC, the builders of M113. Both are amphibious, highly mobile and thinly armoured. Both carry a crew of three, vision devices for day and night observation, and are armed with a 20mm cannon for which 500 rounds are stowed. Since there is no provision for a co-axial machinegun, the gunner can only use 20mm rounds for whatever target he may find. The commander has the use of a pintle-mounted 7·62mm machinegun, but he must be head and shoulders out of the turret to aim and fire.

In the search for the perfect vehicle the US Army has let slip the opportunity to acquire satisfactory, if not ideal, replacements for the M114, which will probably remain in service for a number of years yet, pending development of the ARSV. Possibly simple economics may force a return to the armed Jeep as the recce vehicle of the future.

Left: *The power train has been removed from this M114 via the large access hatches on top and glacis.* / Robin Adshead

Right: *M114 with weapons mounted: armament cannot be fired from under armour but only with the crew half exposed.* / US Army

M113
Armoured Personnel Carrier

Vehicle: M113A1
Crew: 1 + section of 12
Dimensions:
length 4·870m
width 2·690m
height 2·500m
weight 10 930kg
Armament:
main 1 × 12·7mm machinegun
ammunition 2 000 rounds
Mobility:
speed (ground) 68·4kph
 (water) 5·8kph
range 500km
ground pressure ·54kg/cm2

The M113 Armoured Personnel Carrier is probably the most widely used AFV in the Western world, some 43 000 having been produced. Of the major NATO countries only Britain and Portugal do not use the M113 as standard equipment.

In 1956 the Food Machinery Corporation of San Jose, California, started work on a new vehicle to the same operational requirement as the British FV432. They had already been responsible for the M59 and M75 APCs and their long experience in this field enabled them to start production in 1960.

The hull of the M113 is made of cold-rolled aluminium armour plate type 5083, an alloy containing magnesium and manganese. This in itself did not create any weight saving compared with steel plate giving the same immunity against attack. In order to achieve the same immunity the aluminium plate had to be three times as thick as steel armour, and steel is roughly three times the density of the alloy. However, the thickness of the alloy plates gave them sufficient rigidity to allow the designers to dispense with some of the internal structural members which would have been necessary with steel, leading to a small overall

saving in weight. The comparative softness of the aluminium plate makes it easier to machine than steel and significant savings can be made in manufacturing costs.

The basic M113 APC carries a crew of two – driver and commander– and either a section of 11 men or 6·5 cubic metres of stores. The design has been adapted to carry a wide range of weapons and for many other roles. The versatility of this remarkable vehicle seems inexhaustible and almost every new weapon or equipment seems to end up on or in M113 or one of its variants.

The design is inherently buoyant, with a swimming speed in still water of 5·6kph (3·5mph) derived from track propulsion. A hinged splash board is mounted on the glacis plate. This prevents the pressure of water on the hull forcing the nose down when moving forwards. The first M113 had a Chrysler V-8 gasoline engine, but later versions built since 1964 are powered by a GM V-6 two-stroke diesel. The Allison semi-automatic transmission is common to all versions. The commander has a hatch on the roof, and access for the infantry is by a large hinged ramp door in the rear.

Until the Americans found they were taking very high casualties in Vietnam, the machinegunners firing from the roof mounted ·30in and ·50in Brownings were unprotected. Later a great variety of gun shields were tried out, and it was common to see M113s with piles of sandbags on the roof to give additional protection.

The infantry had no chance to fire their personal weapons from under armour. American tactical doctrine insisted that they should dismount for action, 'to close with the enemy', and no weapon slits were provided. Neither were observation devices, so when they did dismount the infantry had very little idea of the situation into which they were being decanted. It was the classical 'battle taxi', in contrast to the German doctrine of the Panzer Grenadier who fought from his APC as much as possible.

More than one hundred variants of the M113 have been developed, both armoured and unarmoured. Of these many are only minor alterations, such as the addition of weapon and observation slots, and most of the other variants cover different weapon systems. Machineguns from 7·62mm to 12·7mm, cannon from 20mm to 76mm, mortars from 81mm to 120mm, and anti-tank and anti-aircraft missiles are the main weapon changes. Flamethrowers and long range ballistic missile versions are also part of this very versatile family. M113 is not without its faults; it has a high, distinctive and box-like hull, and its immunity to small arms fire is not all it might be. Nevertheless, it has been the cheapest APC in the world for many years, and will continue in service for a long time to come.

The majority of vehicles in NATO service are of a few variants only, although examples of most have appeared in Europe at one time or another.

An M113 of the Italian army heads a battery of M109 SPs on parade in Rome. / Stato Maggiore dell'Esercito

Many of the variants have been experimental or have resulted in very small production runs.

M113A1

The designation of the diesel engined version, otherwise no different from the original M113.

M113 C & R

This Command and Reconnaissance variant developed by FMC in 1963 and 260 were delivered to the Netherlands. It has a lower and shorter hull and carries a 12·7mm (·50in) remotely controlled machinegun on the commander's cupola. Mechanical components are the same as for M113 except for the reduction to four road wheels each side and the provision of a water propulsion unit.

Lynx

Originally known as the M113½, Lynx is a similar vehicle to M113 C & R, and 174 were sold to Canada. The only visible difference from the C & R vehicle is the 7·62mm machinegun mounted on the operator's cupola on the left front of the hull. Both vehicles carry a crew of three men only. User forces have mounted many different weapon systems on these vehicles, including 20mm cannon, 106mm recoilless rifles and ATGW.

M125 and M125A1

These variants are basically the same mortar-carrying vehicle, the latter being the diesel engined version. An 81mm mortar is mounted on a 360° traverse baseplate in the hull and fires through a three part hatch in the roof. The normal ground service baseplate and mounting are stowed on the outside of the hull for use if required. A total of 114 rounds of mortar ammunition are carried.

M548

An unarmoured transport vehicle with a three-man cab at the front and load space behind, the M548 is the standard ammunition carrier for the M107 and M110 heavy SP artillery and has been used for carrying all types of stores. Special variants are equipped to carry bulk fuel, radar and anti-aircraft missile systems. A version has been used by BAC to carry the Rapier anti-aircraft missile system under armour, under a contract for Iran,

but it is not yet bought by any country within NATO. The American Chaparral missile system is also carried on M548.

M577 and M577A1

These variants are identical except for the diesel engine in the latter. It is the Command Vehicle version with a large box hull of greater height than the APC, equipped with desks, mapboards, additional radios and space for a command post staff. A penthouse tent is stowed at the rear and can be extended to give greater accommodation when halted for long periods. A charging engine for signal batteries is stowed externally.

M579

Adapted for use by fitters the M579 mounts an hydraulically operated 1·5ton capacity crane for changing components in the field. It can carry almost two tons of stores and spares and has a crew of two plus one or two fitters.

M806A1

The M806A1 is fitted with an hydraulic recovery winch and a crane similar to that of the M579. It also has a spade at the back of the hull to allow for higher winch pulls.

M741

This is the designation of the M113 hull mounting a Vulcan 20mm cannon, the unit being called the M163 Vulcan Air Defense System. The six-barrelled Vulcan gun has a 360° traverse mounting and elevation from −5° to +80°, allowing it to engage both ground and air targets. It has a rate of fire of up to 3 000 rounds per minute, so ammunition replenishment is a significant factor and would be carried out in operations by the M548.

XM474

A variant which forms a team of four vehicles carrying the Pershing missile system. One vehicle carries the warhead, another the launcher and two the associated electronics. The American and German forces use this type, which will be superseded by the XM688 and XM752 as the Lance missile system takes over from Pershing.

Among the variety of equipments mounted on M113 hulls, the British Green Archer Mortar Locating Radar has been used by the Danish, German and Italian Armies.

The latest variant is the M113A1 Product Improved vehicle, which, for the first time in the series, makes an attempt to turn the 'Battle Taxi' into an Infantry Fighting Vehicle. The upper sides of the hull behind the commander's cupola are inclined for better ballistic protection and provided with observation and firing points for the infantry personal weapons. This version is also made under licence by Oto Melara in Italy.

An M113 of the Bundeswehr comes ashore with its trim vane still rigged for swimming. / Bundesministerium der Verteidigung, Bonn

M107 and M110
Self Propelled Guns

Vehicle: M107
Crew: 5 on vehicle (+8 in support vehicle)
Dimensions:
length 11·256m (overall) 5·72m (hull)
width 3·149m
height 3·679m (to top of barrel)
weight 28 168kg
Armament:
main 1 ×175mm
ammunition 2 rounds
Mobility:
speed (ground) 56kph
range 725km
ground pressure ·81kh/cm²

Vehicle: M110
Crew: 5 on vehicle (+8 in support vehicle)
Dimensions:
length 7·430m (overall) 5·72m (hull)
width 3·149m
height 2·93m (to top of barrel)
weight 26 534kg
Armament:
main 1 ×203mm
ammunition 2 rounds
Mobility:
speed (ground) 56kph
range 725km
ground pressure ·76kg/cm²

Until the changes in global deployment in the mid 1950s brought a requirement for self-propelled artillery to be airportable, all SPs had been based on existing tank hulls. These were readily available, comparatively cheap and had the great advantage of standardisation of spare parts, training and maintenance. However, with troops scattered all over the world, and the vital necessity to be able to support them quickly, the US Army started to think about the advisability of having heavy guns on self-propelled chassis that could be delivered anywhere that their fleet of heavy transport aircraft could reach. In 1957 they started to study the problem, and work went ahead on the use of light alloy hulls using diesel engine power units, the design parent being the Pacific Car and Foundry Company.

Prototypes mounting 175mm and 203mm guns were completed, tested and adopted as the M107

and M110, first production units coming off the line in 1962. The mechanical components are those used in other AFVs, including the M108 and M109 and the M578, and the hull is mainly light alloy. The guns of the M107 and M110 are totally different. The 203mm howitzer of the M110 is a development of the eight inch howitzer of WWI, with a new barrel designed in 1940. It was used on a field carriage during WWII, and then mounted experimentally on several types of tank hull as a self-propelled gun. Since it is a very effective piece, it was dragged out of retirement for mounting on the M110. With a range of 21 miles for its 90·7kg shell, it also has a limited tactical nuclear capability. When mounted on a mobile chassis the gun is fitted with equilibrators which take some of the strain off the elevating mechanism. The hull has a large hydraulically operated spade at the rear which, when in the firing position, is lowered to the ground and dug in by driving the vehicle backwards until it will go no further; then, when the gun is fired, much of the recoil force is absorbed by the earth.

In complete contrast, the 175mm cannon, with its long 60 calibre barrel is a new piece, design work on which started in 1957. However, in the interest of standardisation, the mounting of the 175mm piece uses many parts common with the older weapon, and the automotive chassis and the spade are identical. The 175mm cannon fires a 66·6kg shell to 20 miles, and has a similar nuclear capability to the M110.

Both the M107 and the M110 have a 13 man crew, five of whom travel on the gun carrier, and the remainder on the ammunition carrier which always accompanies the gun. When in action the crews work in the open with no armour protection, although experiments have been made to provide some protection against weather and NBC conditions. The British, German, Italian and Netherlands armies all have both these types in service.

Left: *An M107 ready to fire on exercise in Germany.* / Central Office of Information

Below: *A well used 8-inch howitzer of the US army.*

M109
Self Propelled Gun

Vehicle: M109
Crew: 6
Dimensions:
length 6·612m (gun forward) 6·114m (hull)
width 3·295m
height 3·048m (to turret top)
weight 23 786kg
Armament:
main 1 × 155mm howitzer
ammunition 28 rounds
secondary 1 × 12·7mm machinegun pintle mounted
ammunition 500 rounds
Mobility:
speed (ground) 56kph
(water) 6·43kph
range 360km
ground pressure ·766kg/cm²

The self-propelled howitzer developed rapidly in the postwar years from the artillery piece mounted in a convenient tank hull to the purpose built artillery vehicle. Early types had a limited traverse turret instead of the wartime open topped fighting compartment, but in 1962 the first production model of M109 was built, with a 360° traverse turret. It followed the M108 which was a 105mm piece similarly mounted in an all-round traverse turret.

The M126 155mm gun elevates from −3° to +75° and has a maximum range of 14 700 metres. It can fire up to three rounds a minute, which is good for such a calibre, although the French 155mm GCT SP howitzer can get up to eight rounds off per minute for five minutes with its auto-loader (the French gun team then take half an hour to reload the magazine with 42 complete rounds).

The gun mounting is a hydro-pneumatic variable recoil type, recoil distance varying from 36in to 23in depending on the elevation of the barrel. The projectile is loaded by a semi-automatic hydraulic rammer and the charge by hand. The breech block is locked by an interrupted thread, and firing is by pulling on a lanyard. Just behind the large double baffle muzzle brake is a very distinctive circular fume extractor.

Turret traverse is hydraulic, though an emergency handwheel is provided, and elevation is also normally hydraulic, with a manual pump as standby. The layer has an M118C direct fire elbow periscope and an XM42 offset periscope, while the commander has a panoramic periscope.

M109 has a crew of six. The driver controls the vehicle with a half steering wheel that operates clutch and brake steering in first and second ratios and geared steering in third and fourth. The vehicle is built of aluminium armour by the Allison Division of General Motors and has a GM V8 turbocharged diesel engine and an Allison transmission. Weighing only 23 tons, it has a maximum speed of 35mph and a range of 220 miles, with excellent cross country mobility. Not inherently buoyant, it can be fitted with a floatation kit of nine air bags, attached four each side and one at the front, with wave boards outside the airbags. A blower assembly inflates the bags and can maintain the 2psi pressure needed even if the bags are punctured by bullets. When swimming crews are supposed to wear lifejackets.

Over 2 000 M109s were built and it has become a standard artillery equipment throughout NATO. The Bundeswehr guns are made by Rheinmetall, and have horizontal sliding breech blocks, while many of the Italian Army vehicles are fitted with guns made in Italy by Oto Melara. M109 will probably be replaced in most NATO forces by the self-propelled version of the new FH70 when that comes into service.

Left: *A battery of the newer long-barrelled version of the M109 in action.* / Robin Adshead

Right: *M109s of the German army in action.* / Bundesministerium der Verteidigung, Bonn

M88
Armoured Recovery Vehicle

The hull, above track guard level, is a purpose designed shell with large access doors, a commander's cupola and complex air louvres over the engine compartment. It is usually hung about like a Christmas tree with spare road wheels, sprocket rings, return rollers and track plates, for these are items most likely to need replacement on the tank casualties that the M88 is called upon to recover. At the front is an hydraulically operated dozer blade for digging tanks into or out of fire positions and trouble. One or more machineguns can be pintle-mounted on the roof for local protection.

An A-frame, normally carried lowered over the rear, can be erected at the front. It can support weights of 6 078kg, and when itself supported by the dozer blade, can take the maximum lifting capacity of the hoisting winch, up to 25 tons. The main recovery winch has 61 metres of cable and can pull up to 40 823kg at 8·3m/min.

M88 will remain in service until well into the 1980s. A trial programme has been going on for some years to use the mechanical components of the M60 tank, and if this is successful all remaining M88s will be retrofitted to the new specification. Many have already had their gasoline engines replaced by the AVDS 1790 diesel engine.

Vehicle: M88
Crew: 4
Dimensions:
length 8·267m (including dozer blade)
width 3·428m
height 3·220m (including machinegun) 2·921m (top of cupola)
weight 50 800kg
Armament:
main 1 × 12·7mm machinegun
ammunition 1 500 rounds
Mobility:
speed (ground) 48kph
range 360km
ground pressure ·74kg/cm^2

Based on the M48 power train and running gear, the M88 ARV started production by Bowen-McLaughlin-York in 1961, after seven years development — nearly as long as for a new design of MBT. By the time production ceased in 1964 over 1 000 units had been built. They have given excellent service in all theatres, and are still very much sought after by all users of American MBTs.

Left: *M88 recovering an M60.* / Robin Adshead

Below: *An M88 armoured recovery vehicle winches out a Saladin that fell into a hole in the river bed.*

M578
Recovery Vehicle

Based on the same chassis as the M107 and M110 self-propelled guns, the M578 was built by three companies in the USA. Production started in 1962. It is fitted with a crane of 13 620kg lifting capacity in a 360° slewing turret. The recovery winch has a maximum bare drum line pull of 27 240kg when using the rear mounted spade. The suspension can be locked out to transmit lifting forces directly on to the ground.

Vehicle: M578
Crew: 3
Dimensions:
length 6·420m (including crane) 5·937m (hull)
width 3·149m
height 3·000m
weight 24 470kg
Armament:
main 1 × 12·7mm machinegun
ammunition 500 rounds
Mobility:
speed (ground) 59·5kph
range 725km
ground pressure ·71kg/cm^2

Left: *An M578 in latest US Army camouflage and markings.* / Robin Adshead

Below: *M578 light armoured recovery vehicle prepares to recover an M113 APC that failed to make the river crossing.*

Sheridan
Reconnaissance Tank

Vehicle: M551 Sheridan
Crew: 4
Dimensions:
length 6·299m overall
width 2·819m
height 2·946m
weight 15 830kg
Armament:
main 1 × 152mm gun/launcher
ammunition 19 conventional rounds and 10 Shillelagh missiles
secondary 1 × 7·62mm coaxial and 1 × 12·7mm machinegun on cupola
ammunition 3 000 × 7·62mm and 1 000 × 12·7mm
Mobility:
speed (ground) 70kph
(water) 5·8kph
range 600km
ground pressure ·49kg/cm2

The new American reconnaissance tank of the 1960s had to be mobile, hard-hitting, reliable and simple to maintain. It took eight years to get from the initial stages of design to the first prototype, which was built by the Allison Division of General Motors in 1966.

Standardised as the M551, the Sheridan has a 300hp turbo-charged multi-fuel engine which gives a power/weight ratio of 20hp per ton and a top speed of 43mph. It has a useful battle range and the ability to swim at 3·5mph using track propulsion and a buoyancy screen.

The hull is built of aluminium armour, and aluminium is also used for the 4-speed crossdrive casing, the engine block and crossflow radiators. Its battle weight of 15 tons means that it is air-portable and air-droppable, and gives the low ground pressure of 0·49kg/cm .

The turret is the only major structural com-

Experience of heavy commander losses in Vietnam led to the extra armour round the cupola of the M551. / Robin Adshead

ponent made of steel. It has a good ballistic shape, with its curved sides, but the undercut lower sides could make a good bullet trap. The commander's cupola has a ring of vision blocks and a powered traverse facility. The gunner has two independent vision and sighting devices, a ×8 direct fire telescope and a passive night periscope sight. Four smoke grenade dischargers are fitted each side. The boxes seen on the outside of the turret each side are reserve machinegun ammunition stowage.

A unique feature of Sheridan is the rotating driver's hatch which incorporates three periscopes for use when closed down. The central periscope can be changed for an IR night driving device when required. The driver has two pedal controls, brake and accelerator, and a T-bar steering unit. The Allison transmission has a pivot turn capability. Unlike most American tanks, the Sheridan track is of the single pin variety.

The combat effectiveness of an AFV depends on its armament, and it is this department that most of the troubles with Sheridan have been experienced. The main armament is the 152mm Shillelagh gun/missile launcher system, which is supposed to combine the advantages of a large conventional round with those of a long range ATGW. As with most compromises the result is that it performs neither role well, being both complicated and far from robust.

To give sufficient penetrating power to the missile a large diameter warhead was necessary. The conventional round to be fired from the same tube is therefore much larger than is really necessary, having a considerable 'overkill' against most normal HE targets. As a result of the size of the ammunition only 19 rounds and 10 missiles can be carried — not many shots to last a 24-hour battle day.

To eliminate the problem of the disposal of large cartridge cases from the turret the conventional round has a combustible case. This has caused many of the problems and lengthy delays in development; the case proved fragile, prone to absorb damp and to incomplete combustion, leaving smouldering fragments in the chamber which could ignite the charge of the next round loaded. Both open and closed breech scavenging systems have been tried to eliminate this danger.

It is the long range Shillelagh missile of high lethality which gives Sheridan its tank-killing power. It has an automatic command-to-line-of-sight guidance system, but unlike the other in-service ATGW, Shillelagh uses an infrared command link. This more complicated and more expensive than the wire-guidance links of HOT, TOW and Swingfire, and it is thought that spurious IR sources, of which there are many on a battle-field, could jam or otherwise interfere with the command link. As with other automatic guidance systems the gunner has only to hold the target in the centre of his sight to achieve a hit, and when a hit occurs, target destruction is assured.

Secondary armament consists of one coaxial 7·62mm machinegun and one ·50in machinegun on the commander's cupola, though it is not built in to the cupola as in the M48 and M60, but must be fired from the 'head and shoulders out' position. In an effort to reduce the vulnerability of the commander, many Sheridans have been fitted with a semi-circular gun shield, which brings the height of the vehicle to just over 10ft.

It is difficult to identify a role for which Sheridan is ideally suited. It is too large to be the spearhead of a reconnaissance unit, though it has good mobility. With its heavy firepower it would be useful as a fire support vehicle for forward elements if it carried enough rounds. Sheridan's ability to kill MBTs at long range is more in line with the role of the battle tank itself, but with immunity only against small arms, splinter and blast, it would not last long in such company.

The day of the major airborne assault is past, at least in the context of NATO, and airborne reinforcement is more applicable to 'brush-fire' wars than to the European theatre. Sheridan falls between the strength of an MBT and the small size of a reconnaissance vehicle.

Sheridan has seen service in Vietnam, but since the ATGW capability was not needed there, the missile system was removed in favour of more conventional ammunition. Used only by the American Army, production ceased in 1970 after 1 662 units had been built.

Left: *Not the 4th of July but firing the 152mm weapon at night.* / Robin Adshead

Below: *M551 Sheridan prototype, Pilot No 12. The smoke grenade dischargers and the driver's periscope have not been fitted.* / EMC

YP408
Armoured Personnel Carrier

Vehicle: YP408
Crew: 2 + section of 10
Dimensions:
length 6·230m
width 2·400m
height 2·37m including machinegun, 1·80m to top of hull
weight 12 000kg
Armament:
main 1 ×12·7mm machinegun
ammunition as required
Mobility:
speed (ground) 80kph
range 500km

The Netherlands determined to utilise to the full the capability of their own industry, and in 1956 asked Van Doornes Bedrijfswagenfabriek BV of Eindhoven (DAF) to design a wheeled APC based as far as possible on commercial components.

DAF took the DS 575 diesel engine used in their heavy truck range, and the transmission from their cross-country trucks as the basic units. The drive goes through an auxiliary gearbox with high and low ratios, to transfer cases on each side of the hull. From the transfer cases (in which there is a mechanism for engagement of the front wheel drive) propshafts in the form of an 'H' drive take the power to the front pair of wheels, and to the rear bogie. The final drive at each wheel station is by worm gears.

The suspension of the YP408 is unique. The front pair of wheels are independently suspended on trailing arms with transverse torsion bars. The second pair, which are steerable but not driven, are also independently suspended, but the torsion bars are longitudinal. The third and fourth pairs of wheels form a bogie, with wheel stations at each end of a walking beam which is suspended on conventional leaf springs.

The hull is of steel armour, giving protection against small arms fire, and is well sloped. Its over-all height is low, and troops can fire their personal weapons from roof hatches rather than weapon ports. Access is by two rear doors. Just behind the driver, who can operate 'head out' or closed down, is a rotating cupola with two semi-circular hatches which can be locked in the vertical position to give the vehicle commander some flank protection. The only armament carried is a ·5in (12·7mm) Browning machinegun on a DAF-designed mounting which can be fired by the commander only when his head and shoulders are exposed.

The YP408, which has been adopted only by the Netherlands Army, has been built as APC, Command Vehicle, Ambulance (in which role it carries no armament), Stores Carrier and as tractor for the 120mm Brandt Mortar; in the latter role it tows the mortar on its wheeled carriage and carries the crew and 50 rounds of ammunition.

Left: *The YP408 APC is in service with the Dutch army.* / DAF

Below: *This version of the YP408 is armed with the American TOW anti-tank missile. Note the multiple split hatches in the roof.* / Bart Vanderveen Collection

The right hand M60 is illuminating the target for the left hand tank on the practice range. / Robin Adshead